FAIRY STORIES

TOP·TEN

MICHAEL COLEMAN

Illustrated by **Michael Tickner**

Scholastic Children's Books,
Commonwealth House, 1-19 New Oxford Street, London WC1A 1NU
a division of Scholastic Limited
London - New York - Toronto - Sydney - Auckland
Mexico City ~ New Delhi ~ Hong Kong

First published in the UK by Scholastic Ltd

ISBN 0 590 11293 7

Typeset by Falcon Oast Graphic Art, East Hoathly, East Sussex.
Printed by Cox & Wyman, Reading, Berks.

10 9 8 7 6 5 4 3 2 1

Contents

Introduction

Welcome. Come a little closer. Closer still. That's it.

Now then, tell me if I'm right. You've picked this book up, but in your heart you're thinking that it's going to be all gooey and babyish, and that you'll be putting it straight back down again. Yes?

Well, so you might – but not because it's too gooey. If you do put it down again it will be because it's too *gory*!

Because, you see, the stories I'll be telling you won't be the sugar-coated kind you've probably heard from your parents and teachers, or seen on the television, or read in slushy books with gorgeous princesses and towering castles on their covers.

WADDAYA MEAN, IM _TOO_ GORGEOUS?!!

7

Oh, no. From me you'll be getting the *uncensored* versions, the stories as they were told hundreds of years ago, before they were first written down. In those days they were thought of as stories for everybody. . .

- Poor peasants would tell stories to liven up their boring work in the fields or the spinning rooms.
- Families would entertain each other through the long winter evenings by sitting around a crackling fire telling terrible tales.
- Merchants and travellers would share stories with people they met on their journeys.

- In well-to-do homes, children would be told stories by their nurses that helped them drop off to sleep – or scared them stiff if they didn't!
- Fairy tales were even told in church! Priests would use them to teach lessons on how (and how not) to live good lives.

Because these stories weren't just for children, but for everybody, they weren't watered-down. Some had gruesome versions. Some had rude versions. Some had gruesome *and* rude versions!

So, here they come. The top ten fairy stories, chosen for their popularity over hundreds of years. The best-known fairy tales. Stories you might *think* you already know inside out.

But do you?

Let's begin, then.

Once upon a time. . .

Story 10: Hansel and Gretel

...There were two children, Hansel and Gretel. Our number 10 tale comes from Germany, but stories like it are known in many European countries.

The story of Hansel and Gretel is easily 200 years old, but really became famous in 1893 when the composer Engelbert Humperdinck decided to turn it into an opera. It was to be an opera for children, though, so squeamish Hump the Chump thought that for their sake he should miss a bit out.

Which bit? The opening bit. Because, you see, all the problems Hansel and Gretel face are caused by their truly awful parents. Because of them, the two children come face to face with one of the ghastliest witches ever described. She is cruel, she is calculating, and she knows exactly what she wants: a delightful meal of plump roast boy.

Humperdinck realized that story would make a great opera. So if television had been around in those days, there's no doubt that somebody would have snapped it up for a dramatic TV reconstruction programme, complete with a concerned-looking presenter. A programme with a script something like this . . .

Open with dramatic music. Mix to shots of frightened onlookers, standing outside a cottage deep in the woods. Through the windows there's a flickering red glow, coming from an oven door.

Cut to shot of a small casket being carried out from the cottage – the sort of casket used to hold the grey ashes of somebody who's been hideously burned alive . . .

Presenter steps forward with solemn look on his face and addresses the viewer solemnly.

Presenter: Tonight's "Emergency!!!" is a tale of heroism which will amaze you. It features two children, Hansel and Gretel, who found themselves in a seemingly hopeless situation. Trapped and afraid, with no way of calling for help, they thought they were faced with the certainty of a horrible death.

How did they come to be in this terrifying position? See for yourselves. But be warned: some scenes in this reconstruction are not for those of a nervous disposition. And yet our story begins in an ordinary cottage on an ordinary night . . .

The family's cottage. Midnight.

An ordinary bedroom in an ordinary cottage. Hansel and Gretel are tucked up in their beds. Soft voices are coming from behind the wall.

Hansel: Gretel! Listen!

Gretel: (*Sleepy*) Go to sleep, Hansel!

Hansel: Listen, I say! Or we'll both be asleep – for good!

The voices from behind the wall get louder.

Father: That's it. Our money's all gone. What can we do?

Mother: The only thing possible. Take our children deep into the woods tomorrow and leave them there.

Father: Our children? My dear daughter? My super son? What are you saying? They'll be savaged, torn to shreds by the wild animals!

Mother: It's us or them. Give those animals shredded feet for breakfast, that's what I say. Then with two fewer mouths to feed, *we* might not starve.

Father: I can't! I can't do it!

Mother: Then, husband, you'd better start making a coffin large enough for all four of us. Nag, nag, nag . . .

Father: (*In tears*) All right, I agree! We'll do it first thing tomorrow.

The garden. Later that night.

An ordinary garden outside the ordinary cottage. Hansel is scrabbling about on his knees.

Gretel: This is no time to be gardening, you idiot!

Hansel: I'm not. I'm collecting silver-coloured pebbles . . .

Presenter appears, looking stony-faced.

Presenter: Clear-headed Hansel was putting together a survival kit – an essential for any child who suspects that their plotting parents are planning to abandon them in a wood . . .

The wood. Next morning.

Hansel, Gretel and their parents are shuffling through a silent wood. Trees tower above them, so that only a few shafts of sunlight can break through to relieve the

gloom. **As they walk along, Hansel and Gretel are dropping their silver pebbles. Finally, they stop. The children look frightened.**

Father: Well, your mother and I are off to chop some wood. We'll see you two later. Have a rest. You'll probably sleep like logs.

Mother: And don't worry if we're rather a long time, darlings . . .

They leave, quickly. Presenter comes out from behind a tree, looking ashen.

Presenter: Of course the children knew they weren't coming back. But their survival plans had been well thought out . . .

The cottage. Later that night.

The children burst through the door.

Gretel: Father! Mother! We're back! Hansel laid a trail of pebbles for us to follow.

Father: Stone me. I mean, wonderful!

Mother: Yes, great. Really great . . .

The cottage. Midnight, a few months later.
As before: Hansel and Gretel in bed, voices coming from behind the wall. Presenter climbs out from a wardrobe, looking shirty.

Presenter: And so their wicked plan was foiled. But a few months later, when food was low once more, those pitiful parents tried again . . .

Mother: Take them far deeper into the wood this time, you fool! So far in they'll never find their way out! Snap, snarl, bite . . .

Father: What if I don't agree? Bleat, bleat, baa . . .

Mother: You agreed last time, so you've got to agree this time! Nag, nag, nag, extra-nag, nag . . .

Father: All right, I agree. Whimper, whimper, snivel . . .

The kitchen. Later that night.
Hansel and Gretel creep downstairs. They try the cottage door. It's locked.

Hansel: We can't get out. What are we going to do?

Gretel: Use your loaf, boy. We'll lay a trail of breadcrumbs instead.

The wood. Next morning.

Deeper in the wood this time, so deep it's difficult to see anything. Wild animals are howling in the distance. As they walk, the two children are dropping breadcrumbs on the ground.

Father: This is far enough. Well my little darlings, your strong, fearless father and your lovely, caring mother are off to chop wood again.

Mother: And this time we may be an *awfully* long time . . .

They disappear. Presenter appears from behind a willow, weeping.

Presenter: And so, once again, Hansel and Gretel were abandoned. But this time, when they looked for the trail they'd left . . .

Hansel: The bread! The birds must have eaten it! It's gone!

The wood. Two days later.
Even further into the wood. Presenter steps out through the door of a cottage made of gingerbread. He's looking sweet.

Presenter: And so, for two days, the poor children wandered deeper and deeper into the wood until, hungry and thirsty, they saw a snow-white bird. Following it, they were led to a cottage that not only looked good enough to eat ... it was good enough to eat!
Gretel: Hansel! This lump of roof tastes delicious! I'm going to have a night on the tiles!
Hansel: And this window I've just put my fist through is made of sugar! One lump or twenty, Gretel?

Presenter looks through the broken window, looking pained.

Presenter: Stranded in a fairy-tale wood, the two children realized how important it was to keep up their energy levels. Be warned, though. If you're ever in the same situation, settle for picking a few blackberries. Looking for a house you can eat may seem a good idea, but it isn't. They are death-traps, set by evil witches to entice children into their clutches. For no sooner had the children begun to eat than they heard somebody trill . . .

Witch: Tip-tap, tip-tap, who raps at my door?

The door squeaks open. A very old woman appears. She has red eyes and walks on crutches.

Witch: Ah, I thought I smelled children! Enter, my little loves! Call me an old witch if you like, but I just had this feeling that somebody was going to call on me today. Now then, I have a lovely meal all ready for you. And soft beds with clean white sheets for you to sleep in . . .

A bedroom in the witch's house.

The children eat the meal, then jump into the beds.

Hansel: We're in heaven, Gretel!

Witch: (To herself) You will be soon, my dear. I can't wait to get my teeth into his chubby red cheeks!

The kitchen. Next morning.

Presenter: Yes, eating the two children was her plan. The moment Hansel woke next morning the witch dragged him out of his bed and threw him into a dark and filthy cage.

Hansel: Help! Let me out!

Witch: What? Think yourself lucky, boy! Out there in the wood, you'd have starved to death by now. But I'm going to feed you well. Only until you're nice and plump, of course. Then I'm going to feed *myself* well! On you!

Gretel: What are you going to do with me?

Witch: You? You're going to be my slave, dearie. Now start working!

Presenter comes out of the loo, looking flushed.

Presenter: The children were trapped – and all because they'd ignored the first rule of survival in a fairy-tale wood: "Know your witches"! Witches have a keen sense of smell, red eyes, and like nothing better for their supper than a boy-be-que. All the evidence was there. Don't fall into the same trap yourselves. For a fact sheet on witch-watching, write to the address you'll be given at the end of the programme.

The kitchen. Two weeks later.

Hansel is still caged. Gretel is getting aged. The witch is enraged.

18

Presenter: And so poor Gretel worked, fetching and carrying for the witch, and being fed nothing more than the odd crab's claw. As for Hansel, the condemned boy was eating a hearty breakfast every day – not to mention hearty dinners and suppers ...

Witch: That's another batch of chicken drumsticks you've polished off, Hansel! Let's see if you're fat enough to eat yet, boy. Stick your finger out through the bars!

Presenter appears, counts Hansel's fingers, and looks hand-sum.

Presenter: Hansel still had his wits about him. Instead of his own finger, he poked a chicken bone out through the bars for the witch to test. With her bad eyesight, she was fooled.

Witch: Still thin, boy! No point cooking you yet!

The kitchen. Another two weeks later.

Presenter: And so the children managed to survive – until the day the witch tested Hansel and he used his trick once more. Believing him to be as thin as ever, she lost her patience ...

Witch: Oh, you'll just have to do! I can't wait any longer to eat you. Now, shall I have you boyled? No, baked in the oven, I think. Gretel, open that oven door!

(To herself) And I'm hungry
enough to eat the girl as well!
**Close-up on the witch's oven.
The flames are burning fiercely.**

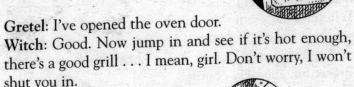

Gretel: I've opened the oven door.
Witch: Good. Now jump in and see if it's hot enough,
there's a good grill . . . I mean, girl. Don't worry, I won't
shut you in.

**Presenter appears, holding
a pan and looking saucy.**

Presenter: Gretel didn't believe her. What she did next
was an object lesson in how to behave if you're faced
with being shoved into a red-hot oven. For a start, she
kept a cool head. . .
Gretel: I'm stupid, Mrs Witch. I don't know how to get
in the oven.
Witch: What? Don't they teach you anything at school
nowadays? That opening is big enough for me to get in!
Gretel: Can you show me how, then?
**The witch climbs in. Gretel slams the door shut tight
then releases Hansel from the cage. Searching around
they find the witch's hoard of jewels.**

Hansel: You're a gem, sister!

They race out of the front door. Close-up on the oven as the witch, howling horribly, is burned to ashes. When it's all over, the presenter appears in the oven, looking very steamed-up.

Presenter: And so the two children made their escape and, with the help of a friendly duck who carried them across a lake, found their way home. There they discovered that their mother had died and that their father, poor thing, had spent the whole time feeling really, really sad about what he'd done. He cheered up a lot when he saw the witch's riches, though, and they all lived happily ever after.

There you are, then. Dramatic stuff indeed and a splendid story for this, the last episode in the current series of *Emergency!!!* So, it only remains for me to say good-night and look forward to joining you again for the next series.

TV Executive appears, looking switched-on.

TV Executive: There won't be a next series. Sorry.
Presenter: No next series? Then . . . what about me?

TV Executive shrugs and leaves.

Presenter: Hey, let me out of this oven! Help! Emergency!!!

Tell me more

- The main change to later versions of this story was to turn the children's nasty mother into a nasty stepmother. Why? To stop children believing that a real mother could be so cruel. But in the original story, wicked Mummy it was. And let's face it, real Daddy didn't take a lot of persuading did he?
- One version of this story had a charming little touch. Instead of poking out a chicken bone for the witch to test, Hansel holds out a twig from an elder tree. Why? Because then when the old hag digs her nails into it the red sap that oozes from the twig looks just like blood!
- Typically, parents and teachers telling this story to children would turn things round and say if Hansel and Gretel hadn't scoffed the witch's house, she wouldn't have caught them. Lesson: that's what happens if you're greedy!

Top Facts 10: The top ten tale-tellers

"I'm going to be an executioner when I grow up!'

"Not me. Too much hanging around for my liking. I'm going to be a chariot driver."

"Oh, that'd drive me round the bend. I'm going to be a writer. I'm going to write stories that will still be told hundreds and hundreds of years from now!"

Where did fairy stories come from? When were they thought up? Who by? How have they been handed down over the years? Here are some of the theories experts have put forward. Which do you think is the right one?

- The stories must date back to the times of the dinosaurs because they include savage bits about people being eaten, and most humans haven't been cannibals since they lived in caves.

- The stories *can't* be that old because they feature things like castles and people getting married.

- The stories *all began in the one place*, like India, and spread out from there. That's why the same kind of stories are known all over the world.

- The stories *didn't* begin in one place. Over time, the same kinds of story have been thought up all over the world – that's why the tales differ from one country to another.

- The stories are *based on real events and real people*, from simple sights like the sun rising and going down to the adventures of a famous king.

- The stories *aren't real at all!* They're based on dreams or nightmares – like the nightmare of being lost in a wood and not being able to get out!

The answer, most experts now agree, is that they're all right ... and all wrong! It depends on the fairy tale. Some are old, some aren't. Some spread from a known country, others didn't. Some are set in the real world, others aren't.

What's important is that, to have survived until today, our top ten European fairy tales had to be told not once, not twice, but year after year after year. Who by? Find out from our

Top ten tale-tellers timetable ...

1. Until 1600 – Everybody!

From the beginning of time, humans tell tales and jokes. In prehistoric playgrounds jokes like "Why did the dinosaur cross the valley? He couldn't – his tyranno was too saurus!" can be heard

Heard. That's the important bit. The jokes and stories are *told*, because most people can't read or write. Hearing a story they like, people then – just like

you with that rude one you heard behind the bike sheds the other day – pass it on to the next person.

What sort of people? Everybody! Farm labourers, washerwomen, sailors, priests, travelling salesmen, courtiers and queens – everybody! In this way the best stories (and the funniest/dirtiest jokes) are handed on until they become stories that everybody knows and tells. They're then said to have become part of the *oral tradition* of the people.

2 From 1000 to 1600 – You peasant!

Gradually the stories become best known by the poor and uneducated – the peasants. Why? Because there were a lot more of them than the rich and learned, of course!

Being uneducated also means that their versions of the stories are ruder and nastier! Why? Because they don't have a stuffy old teacher telling them it's better to say "I fell on my bottom" instead of "I landed on my xxxx!" They tell the stories using the (few) words they know!

As this happens, educated people begin to look down on fairy stories and say they're only fit for "common people".

3 From 1300 to 1600 – "Old wives' tales"

Amongst the masses the top tale-tellers are definitely women! Why? Because in looking after their children (a woman's place is in the home, remember!) women meet each other. While mending clothes in a spinning room or fetching water from a well they swap stories. Stories about lovely princesses spinning gold from straw, about magic frogs at the bottoms of wells . . . and about mean, miserable men!

Older women, with less work to do and more time to spend talking, become particularly expert at telling stories by mixing in plenty of superstition and magic – so much so that by the end of the 16th century the popular stories are called "Old wives' tales".

4 From 1300 onwards – And the moral of this story is. . .

Poor mothers tell the same tales

to their poor children. Rich children hear the stories too, but in their case from a nurse or a governess.

Not exactly the same stories, though. Fairy tales aren't fixed; tellers change the story as and how they want. So, to teach children lessons – about not going off on their own, for instance – a tale is changed. A grown-up story about an ugly witch with a habit of kissing (or worse) any pretty girl daft enough to go near his cave is changed into something like:

"Once upon a time there was an ugly giant who liked nothing better than to capture children who wandered into the woods – a wood rather like the one near our hut, sweetheart – and take them off to his cave where he cooked them and ate them, crunching their bones into little pieces with his long, jagged teeth. . ."

5 From 700 onwards – "The Arabian Nights"
Eastern countries are the first to write their stories down rather than just tell them to each other. The oldest known version

of Cinderella is written in China in 850. The first collection of stories comes from the East too, being written from around 700 onwards. Called *The Arabian Nights*, the collection includes the well-known stories about Aladdin, Sinbad and Ali Baba.

6 From 1550 to 1650 – "Entertaining Nights" and "The Tale of Tales"

In Europe the educated classes – that is, those who can write – still think fairy tales are crude, rude and not worth writing down. Only two collections of written stories exist. They both come from Italy.

The Entertaining Nights, written between 1550 and 1553 by a man named Giovan Straparola, is a selection of rude stories and dirty jokes. He denies that they're old wives' tales – by insisting he wrote them down from the lips of ten young girls!

The other collection is called *The Tale of Tales*, written between 1634 and 1636. Their author is a man, Giambattista Basile, but he seems embarrassed

to admit it. He pretends the 50 stories are being told by thick women! He's the thick one, though. The collection could have made him famous: it includes the classic stories *Cinderella* and *Beauty and the Beast*.

7 The year 1697 – Charles Perrault

A landmark year for fairy tales. A book, *Tales of Olden Times*, written by retired civil servant Charles Perrault (1627–1703), is published in France. It includes *Sleeping Beauty*, *Little Red Riding Hood*, *Bluebeard*, *Puss-in-Boots*, *Diamonds and Toads*, *Cinderella* and *Hop o' my Thumb*.

Perrault's collection is important because he's written the stories seriously. He's cleaned them up, changed them around, and even added little verses at the end explaining the morals of the stories.

From now on, writing and studying fairy tales is "cool". Posh women join in – like Gabrielle-Suzanne Villeneuve, the daughter of a nobleman

who, in 1740, writes an enormously long story filled with details of how well-bred girls should behave. It's called *Beauty and the Beast*.

8 From 1812 to 1857 – The Brothers Grimm

In Germany, Jacob Grimm (1785–1863) and his younger brother Wilhelm (1786–1859) become the most famous collectors of fairy tales. By talking to everybody they meet, from their next-door neighbours onwards, they collect and publish the most popular fairy stories known in Germany. Called *Children's and Household Tales*, the collection includes not only the famous stories told by Perrault, but others like *Hansel and Gretel* and *Snow White*.

In doing this they also show that the history of a people can be studied by looking at the stories they tell. Like Perrault, the Grimms make their mark. From then on, collecting fairy stories and folk tales is "cool" too!

31

9 From 1837 to 1874 – Hans Christian Andersen

During this period the hundreds of stories written by the Danish author, Hans Christian Andersen, are published. They include *The Little Mermaid*, *The Ugly Duckling* and *The Emperor's New Clothes*.

The great Dane not only changes traditional stories, like the tale-tellers before him, he also invents his own. Many of them are set in Denmark. Others are inspired by incidents from his own life – like those featuring his dad's job, shoe-making.

Andersen goes on to become the most famous fairy tale writer of all time ... eventually. When he's first introduced to Jacob Grimm, he finds the collector hasn't heard of him!

10 From today onwards – Me ... and you!

The tradition of telling fairy tales didn't end with Hans Christian Andersen. Ever since, fairy tales old and new have been told and retold.

The same thing is happening

now, at this instant, as you read these words. How? Because in this book I'm telling you the top ten fairy stories – *but in my own way.*

You might then pick the good bits (assuming you think there *are* some good bits!) and tell them to somebody else. Do that and you'll be a tale-teller too!

Michael "Coleman"

Story 9: A history of Tom Thumb

In position number 9 is A history of Tom Thumb. Written by an Englishman, Richard Johnson, in 1620 or thereabouts it features the fantastic adventures of a thumb-sized man.

It's not really a single story though, more a collection of stories (short stories you might say!). What's more, it's a good example of the sort of tale which posh people turned their noses up at. Why? Because it's crude and rude, of course! When told in the market-places of London you can be pretty sure the language was ripe and fruity!

But for the story to be written down and published meant that it would end up with just the sort of educated editor who would want to wash Tom's mouth out with soap and water before letting his words reach the ears of innocent children. The little man's manuscript would have to be covered with more corrections than one of your spelling tests.

In fact, it might have looked a bit like this ...

MY SHORT LIFE
by Tom Thumb

me

A Lowly Birth

Hi! Or maybe that should be "Low"? 'Cos that's what I am. Low. ~~Lower than a slug's xxxxx.~~ (*Very low indeed*).

It's all me dad's fault, ~~the dozy xxxxx~~ (*silly chap*). Wishes for a son doesn't he? But that isn't enough. Oh no! He has to say he'll be happy if he gets one no bigger than his thumb. The ~~xxxxx xxxxxx~~ (*really silly chap*). Why couldn't he say, "no bigger than my ~~bum~~ (*bottom*)"? I'd have been all right then.

Anyway, he doesn't. So Im born thumb-sized and have to learn to put up with it.

I Meet An ~~Old Cow~~ (*Aged Animal*)

Mum wasn't so clever either. The old ~~bat~~ (*dear*) was short-sighted, see.

One day she's making puddings and mixes me into one by mistake. Then she puts it on to boil! I scream blue murder, of course. "~~Xxxxx xxxx! Im xxxxx xxxx~~

35

~~xxxx!~~" (I say! I'm getting "jolly" hot!)
No use. She doesn't hear. So all I can do
is start making the puds go bang. All
BANG! all over the place they go until
the place looks ~~like the~~
~~inside of a cess pit~~ (awfully
messy) and I escape.

Well, after that Mum takes more care.
So one day, when she goes to milk our
cow, she pops me under a thistle
for safety. What happens?
While she's at the udder end,
the cow's eating the thistle —
— and me! I scream blue murder again.
"~~Xxxxx xxxx! I'm in the cow's guts!~~" (I
say! I'm in Daisy's tum-tum!)

Well, this time Mum gets the message.
Off she goes and comes back with a bottle
of her special medicine for making you
~~xxxx~~ (go to the toilet when you're
having trouble) and tips a big spoonful
down the cow's throat......

Next thing I know, I'm on the move! Daisy
lets rip with the biggest ~~xxxx~~ (bottom
burp) you've ever heard and I'm sailing
through the air in the middle of a
~~steaming cowpat~~ (little whoopsie)! I
smelled ~~like a privy~~ (jolly
smelly) for a week!
(On second thoughts, it might be

better if Tom stayed in Daisy's mouth and hopped out when his mummy offered her some medicine and said, "Open Wide!")

I Meet A ~~xxxx xxxx~~ (Jolly Big) Giant

Well, that adventure's nothing compared to what happened next. There I am, walking along the road, when this raven grabs me. It thinks I'm a grain of wheat, the raven lunatic!

Anyway, things get worse. Realizing I'm not wheat he thought (ho-ho) the bird drops me — straight into a giant's castle! Of course, when you're no higher than a ~~sausage dog's sausage~~ (thumb) everybody looks like a giant. But this one was the real thing!

I keep out of his clutches for a while, sweeping the castle cobwebs and the like, but before long he decides I'll make a nice little snack. No chance! As he opens his mouth, I jump straight down his throat and into his ~~belly~~ (tum-tum)! Talk about a short cut!

GIANT

Next I start jumping up and down. "I'm getting ~~a pain in the guts~~ (a tummy ache)!" he hollers.

37

So I jump some more.

"~~I'm going to puke up~~ (I don't feel very well)!" he shouts.

Off he charges, then up to the castle ramparts. He leans over the side and.....

~~Blaaaaaaaaaaaaaagggghhh!~~

~~Out I fly in the centre of a great blob of slimey puke, all mixed up with bits of crunched bone and undigested toenails... and land miles away in the sea!~~

(Oh dear. Perhaps it would be better if Mr Giant went to the water's edge for a little drink to ease his upset tummy and Tom hopped out of his mouth then?)

I Meet A Fish

Well, that got me away from him. But no sooner do I land in the sea than I'm swallowed by a fish!

And no sooner have I been swallowed by the fish than he gets caught and is carted off to be ~~gutted and fried~~ (made into delicious din-dins) on somebody's dinner table. Time to move again! As the fish is slit open, out I jump—

and find myself on the table of none other than good King Arthur himself!! And what happens? He takes me on as his personal midget! Instead of being ~~gutted~~ (jolly upset), I couldn't be happier! I'm like a dog with two ~~xxxx~~ (No, no, no! I'm sorry, I don't think this story is publishable! In my opinion there's no chance at all of Tom Thumb going down in history.)

Tell me more

- After the earliest versions of Tom Thumb appeared, they were almost always cleaned up. The cow episode, in particular, usually had Tom escaping from the cow's mouth. In other words, it was turned into a tale without an end!

- Tom Thumb kept his place in history, though. He's had everything from small cigars to dwarf vegetables named after him. What's more, his name still rings out regularly in London's crowded street markets as traders shove their barrows through the crowds bawling, "Mind yer Tom Thumbs!" How come? Because "Tom Thumb" is Cockney rhyming slang for "bum"!

Top Facts 9: Top ten fairy story ingredients

Search through most fairy stories and you won't find a fairy from start to finish. "That's fairy stupid," I expect you're saying. "So why are they called fairy stories?"

GOOD QUESTION!

It's because fairies are associated with enchantment – magic, in other words – and that's what a fairy story is: a story with magical ingredients. It doesn't matter if these ingredients are good, bad or absolutely disgusting, so long as they're magical!

If you know what these ingredients are, you too can write a fairy story. Don't believe me? Then here's the proof – a top ten fairy tale ingredients section which mixes up a brand-new fairy tale as it goes along!

1 Beginnings
First choose a beginning. Forget about real times and real places, though. You don't want anything like:

"*At 5 o'clock yesterday in Manglewurzel Mews . . .*"

Fairy tales start in a different way, such as:

"*Once upon a time, in a far-away land . . .*"

"*There was a time and no time, and at that time in a land beyond time . . .*"

"*In the olden times, when wishing was having, in a distant country . . .*"

Why? To tell the listener straight away that the story isn't going to be real. It's going to be magical! So, let's have:

Once upon a time in a long-forgotten land...

2 Places

Now choose a setting. The rules are different here. Fairy tales may not have featured real places, like Buckingham Palace or Sherwood Forest, but they did use settings that people would be aware of and appreciate. For example:

• Palaces and castles suggested *riches and romance.*
• Huts and cottages were the opposite, suggesting *poverty and hard work.*
• Woods and forests were *spooky.* (Most people had a wood just down the road and knew how scary the rustlings and howlings could be. Given a choice they wood-n't go near one!)
• Wells – being deep and dark – were *mysterious.*

Let's mix in a bit of glamour.

.....there was a golden palace.

3 Your Majesty!

Why do fairy tales feature kings and queens, princes and princesses? Simple. For the same reason that people nowadays can't read enough about kings and queens, princes and princesses. Because they're glamorous! To a grimy potato-picking peasant and his wife, stories about royalty were magical.

There a King and his daughter lived happily...

4 Vicious villains

Fairy tales are simple stories. They're about good versus bad – and "bad" means a villain! One of these two types would be mixed in:

- A *rotten relative* – a foul father, a sinister stepmother, an ugly uncle.
- A *rotten rival* – somebody the hero or heroine meets and beats, such as a grotty giant, a wicked witch or an 'orrible ogre.

The point about each of these is that the listener could easily imagine them. They might not have any rotten relatives themselves, but they'd know somebody who had. People had no trouble at all with stories about witches (as we'll see in another fact section) because they believed in them! As for giants, they've been in stories since ancient times when it's thought that they were invented as walking versions of natural disasters like earthquakes and volcanoes. Let's have a giant, then.

...until the day when a giant captured the princess and carried her off to his cave where she was forced to spend her days polishing his hoard of gold and silver.

5 Heroes and heroines

Why does any story have a hero or a heroine? To give the reader somebody to root for. Stories have had them since the year dot – well from the times of the ancient Greeks at least, because that's where the word "hero" comes from.

Let's have a hero, then. What's he going to be like? No problem. A common fairy tale hero for Mr Potato Peasant was a chap just like him – flat broke. But . . . what he lacked in money, he more than made up for in brains and courage. These were talents even the poorest could have. So to hear a story about a poor peasant outsmarting a rich and nasty giant? Magic!

The King offered a huge reward for the safe return of his daughter. Three young men came forward. Two were rich and wanted to be richer; they were also stupid. The third was poor but had a mind that was as sharp as a needle; which is why they called him Clever Dick.

6 Pretty ugly!

Fairy-tale descriptions follow a simple pattern:

- Heroes are handsome, heroines are beautiful.
- Villains are ugly.

(This assumes everybody agrees what's meant by "good-looking", of course – which they don't. Somebody I think looks a real cracker might remind you of a warthog on a bad hair day!)

This pattern really annoys many modern readers who say, quite rightly of course, that it simply isn't true. There are many good people around who aren't works of art, just as there are many good-lookers you wouldn't trust any further than you could throw them.

They're missing the point. The tales were telling their audience that *evil* was ugly. If somebody was described as ugly it was because that's what they were on the inside.

A good example is the story of *Goldilocks and the Three Bears*. In early versions it was an ugly old beggar-woman who wandered into a wood and ended up in the bears' house, stealing their food and all the rest. The bears were the goodies of the story, and the woman the villain (people used to think beggars were witches). So when the bears catch the woman, chuck her in a fire, throw her in a pond and finally toss her off a church roof, *that* was the happy ending!

When the story changed into one warning children about the dangers of wandering into dangerous places, the old woman was replaced by a beautiful child – Goldilocks. Now, of course, the bears couldn't be the goodies any more. So now the story's told either in a way that shows the bears as being mean and miserable, or else with them befriending the greedy house-breaker!

So, our story needs to be changed a bit to make it clear who's who:

Once upon a time in a long-forgotten Kingdom, there was a golden palace. There a <u>noble</u> King and his <u>beautiful</u> daughter lived happily ...until one day when an <u>ugly red-haired</u> giant captured the princess and carried her off to his cave where she was forced to spend her days polishing his hoard of gold and silver.

The King offered a huge reward for the safe return of his <u>lovely</u> daughter. Three <u>handsome</u> men came forward. Two were rich and wanted to be richer; they were also stupid. The third was poor but had a mind that was <u>as sharp as a needle</u>; which is why they called him Clever Dick.

7 Challenges

Heroes must face challenges: how else can they prove themselves to be heroes? Typical fairy-tale challenges are:

- facing some ghastly foe (like the beast in *Beauty and the Beast*);
- recovering something that's strongly guarded (as Jack does in *Jack and the Beanstalk*);
- surviving an ordeal (as the children do in *Hansel and Gretel*).

How about a nice gruesome ordeal against a ghastly foe who's strongly guarding a beautiful princess and a stack of treasure?

"Farewell," said the king, sadly. "If the giant guards my daughter as he guards his treasure then I will never see you again. He will batter you to death with his gigantic club then cook you over an open fire.

8 Three of everything

Three challengers, three wishes, three tasks – the number three pops up all over the place in fairy tales. Why?

Possibly because the number three has always been considered magical. Everywhere people looked, things seemed to come in threes . . .

- existence = birth, life and death
- the world = earth, air and water
- humans = body, mind and soul
- nature = animals, vegetables and minerals

Superstitious people still say bad things happen in threes, so it's not surprising that nasty challenges should come along in threes as well. And, in true fairy-tale style, the first two end badly . . .

The giant was waiting for the three young men at the mouth of his cave. "You worms!" he roared. "How can you challenge me? Bah! I will crush your bones into dust! Make a last wish before you die!"

9 I wish . . .

Faced with a big problem, good heroes and heroines are allowed a bit of magical help – like Cinderella got from her fairy godmother. This, more than anything, is what makes a fairy tale.

The list of magical ingredients to choose from is enormous. Here's a few:

- spells cast by a good fairy
- wishes
- magic items and creatures (like geese that lay golden eggs)

Seeing the giant's huge club, the first young man stupidly wished that his body be clothed in the thickest armour. But then he couldn't move at all, and the giant beat him until the armour was squashed flat.

Then it was the second young man's turn. Stupidly he wished that his body be changed so that it could feel no pain. So the giant didn't beat him at all, but stuffed him in his fiery oven and there the young man sat happily until he was completely roasted.

10 Winner

In a fairy tale the hero had to win and the villain had to lose. The last thing the poor peasant wanted to hear was a tale in which the rich got richer. They wanted the rich and wicked to get mangled and for their poor hero to win whatever there was going.

So our tale must end happily, with Clever Dick's cleverness defeating the giant and winning the hand of the fair princess. Which it does, of course . . .

"My wish," said Clever Dick "is that your club be turned into a feather!"

Which is just what happened. The stupid giant started beating Dick over the head with his club as Dick cried, "Harder! I can't feel a thing!" And so it went on hour after hour, until the giant finally dropped down dead.

Clever Dick took the princess back to the King's palace. They were married the next day and, using the giant's gold to buy a palace of their own, lived happily ever after.

49

Story 8: Rumpelstiltskin

The story of the little man Rumpelstiltskin is in number 8 position. This is the name it was known by when the Brothers Grimm heard it in Germany and it can be dated back to at least 1550. The same story has been discovered throughout Europe, though, but with different names for the little man.

Before we start, here – in true fairy-tale style – are three questions:

- Have you ever lied about how clever you are?
- Have you ever been very, very piggishly greedy?
- Have you ever made a promise you knew you couldn't possibly keep?

If you answered "yes" to any of these (or, worse, all three!) then you're just the type this story was devised for. Why? So that, having heard it, you'd be too terrified to do any of these things again!

There are three "not-very-goodies", one "definitely-baddie", and a servant – and the only one who comes out of the story with any credit is the servant. As for the others, they are all rather unpleasant in their different ways; but only one of them gets the punishment he really deserves.

A very nasty punishment as it happens. So nasty that, if it wasn't a story, there'd need to be an inquest to discover precisely how it all came about . . .

A Suspicious Death
DARK FOREST CORONER'S COURT
OFFICIAL TRANSCRIPT OF INQUEST
PROCEEDINGS

DECEASED: MR. RUMPEL-STILTS-KIN
THE HUT ON THE HILL
DARK FOREST
PRESIDING CORONER: Mr C.M.B. De'Ath

The coroner made his opening statement.

CORONER: Where a death is not due to natural causes – and the death of Mr Rumpelstiltskin was just about as unnatural as they come – an inquest must be held to find out the facts. It's my job to discover the long and the short of it. That is what I propose to do. Call the first witness!

Testimony of: THE BOASTFUL MILLER
CORONER: Mr Miller, you are the father of the Queen?

THE MILLER: I am, yer honourable. But she weren't the queen when she was living wiv me, just a beautiful miller's daughter. But beauty don't pay the bills, so we was poor.

CORONER: You were insolvent?

THE MILLER: Too right! We didn't have money for anything, let alone glue!

CORONER: So what did you do about it?

THE MILLER: Well, your honour. I knows now it was wrong, but, well, I just happened to bump into the King one day and he looked at me like I was just a poor miller. . .

CORONER: You were a poor miller.

THE MILLER: Yeh, I know, but I didn't want to admit it, did I? I mean, I wanted him to think I was a bit, y'know, special. So I did a little bit of boasting. I told him my daughter could turn straw into gold.

CORONER: You spun him a story, in other words! And, hearing it, the King commanded you to bring her to him, did he not?

THE MILLER: That's right. I could have kicked meself, I didn't expect him to do that. I didn't know he was ...

CORONER: As greedy as you were boastful? We shall see. Call the King!

Testimony of HIS GREEDY MAJESTY, THE KING

CORONER: Surname?

THE KING: King.

CORONER: First names?

THE KING: His Majesty, The.

CORONER: So, Your Majesty, what happened when you called the miller's daughter to your palace?

THE KING: Good heavens man, what do you think I did! Locked her in a chamber with a spinning wheel and a pile of straw, of course! "Spin that into gold by tomorrow morning," I said, "or else!"

CORONER: Or else what?

THE KING: Or else I'd have her executed. All

right, I know it wasn't a very nice thing to say, but I am . . .

CORONER: Greedy?

THE KING: The King! I am the King! I can say what I want! Anyway, I didn't have to do it, did I? Next morning, there she was surrounded by the biggest mound of gold I'd ever seen – well, until then.

CORONER: You've seen a bigger pile since?

THE KING: Er, yes. Because the next night I shut her up with a bigger pile of straw. And . . . all right, all right, told her she'd be executed if she didn't turn that lot into gold.

CORONER: Your majesty! How greedy could you get?

THE KING: Quite a lot greedier, actually. When she did the trick for a second time, I couldn't believe my luck. So the third night I shut her up in the biggest chamber in the whole palace, crammed to the ceiling with as much straw as I could squeeze in.

CORONER: And threatened her with death again?

THE KING: Really, my good man! I'm not heartless! Besides, a woman with a talent such as hers was far too valuable to lose. No, I told her she would receive the finest prize imaginable – me! Yes, if she spun that lot into gold I said I'd marry her and make her queen.

CORONER: And spin it all into gold she did. But how? That's what I'd like to know. Call the Queen!

Testimony of HER MAJESTY, THE QUEEN

CORONER: You are Her Majesty the Queen?

THE QUEEN: One is now, sir. But on the night the King first shut me away, one was a very different person. Then one was just a helpless, hopeless miller's daughter, who couldn't spin a coin let alone spin straw into gold. As one sat in that cold, dark chamber one could only see one outcome next morning – the executioner's axe! One thought one was for the chop.

CORONER: Cut it out, Your Majesty! Surely, you're joking?

THE QUEEN: One certainly is not. One is a queen, and queens are famous for not being amused! When that nasty little man appeared, one was crying not laughing.

CORONER: Nasty little man? Why not call him by his name.

THE QUEEN: One didn't know his name then, did one? All one knew was that when he offered to spin the straw for me, one couldn't have cared less what his name was. And when he settled for one's necklace in payment, one could have cheered!

CORONER: So, it was the strange little man who spun the first chamber full of straw. And the other two?

THE QUEEN: Those as well. The second night one paid him with one's ring. But on the third night one was right out of possessions. So one had no option but to agree to his suggestion.

CORONER: His suggestion?

THE QUEEN: To give him one's first baby after one became Queen.

CORONER: Outrageous! And you agreed to this?

THE QUEEN: Too right! Don't forget, one was on a promise of being made Queen – not to mention getting one's half-share of the gold one had seen the King stash away. Besides, one never expected it to happen. One couldn't believe that when it came to it the little man would be so cruel as to tear a sweet, innocent baby from its mother's arms. But he was.

One year after one married the King and our precious baby was born, he returned . . .

CORONER: And demanded your child?

THE QUEEN: Yes! One pleaded with him. One offered him all one's riches. And all one's husband's riches . . .

The KING was heard to splutter something, but the words were unclear.

CORONER: Not enough?

THE QUEEN: No. He said he wanted one's child, nothing else would do. One wept and groaned, for by then one had learned that a human life is worth more than all the money in the world. But all he would grant me was three days in which one had to guess his name. If one failed, one's baby would be his to keep for ever.

CORONER: Guess his name, eh? So what did

you try? U.R. Horrible, things like that?

THE QUEEN: Odd names at first. Caspar, Melchior, Balthassar.

CORONER: Odd! They're my names!

THE QUEEN: Yes, well. None of them were right. So on the second day one tried some really wild ones . . .

CORONER: Ah. "Ivor Nasty-Temper", that sort of thing?

THE QUEEN: Whalebone! Sheep-shank! Ribs-of-Beef! But they were all wrong. So, unable to think of any more, one sent one's servant out into the country to collect any name that one had not tried.

At this, the QUEEN burst into tears. She left the stand while she recovered.

CORONER: Call the Queen's servant!

Testimony of the SERVANT
CORONER: Now then, you lowly crumb, you mean minion, what have you got to say for yourself?

SERVANT: On the edge of the forest I saw a little house. In front of the little house I saw a little man. The little man was singing a little song. So, very little really.

CORONER: What was the song about?

SERVANT: Ah, that was the interesting bit. It went:

TODAY I STEW,
AND THEN I'LL BAKE,
TOMORROW I SHALL
THE QUEEN'S CHILD
TAKE,
AH! HOW FAMOUS IT IS
THAT NOBODY KNOWS
THAT MY NAME IS
RUMPELSTILTSKIN.

Continued testimony of HER MAJESTY, THE QUEEN

THE QUEEN: After one heard about the song, one almost looked forward to the little man's arrival. Then he came, and asked, "For the third and final time, before I take your child from your arms, what is my name?"

CORONER: And you said ... Rumpelstiltskin!

THE QUEEN: Not at first. One wasn't in the mood. One fancied annoying him like he'd annoyed one. So first I asked if his name was Conrad. Then, Hal. Last of all, and just as his bony little hands were reaching out for one's baby, one said, "Is it ... Rumpelstiltskin?"

CORONER: Er ... I assume it was?

THE QUEEN: Oh, it was! One felt wonderful! And you should have seen him! What a temper! Hearing his name he screamed, he ranted, he flung his arms and he stamped his feet!

CORONER: Didn't like the boot being on the other foot, obviously.

THE QUEEN: He stamped those feet so hard

that one of them went through the floorboards. This made him even angrier. He pulled at that foot, trying to get it out. But it wouldn't budge.

CORONER: Bless my sole!

THE QUEEN: Still he pulled, though. He pulled and pulled and screamed and howled, until — oh, it quite put one off one's dinner — he ripped himself apart! And that, your honour, is how Rumpelstiltskin met his end.

CORONER'S VERDICT

CORONER: This unhappy case has been a mess from top to bottom — rather like Mr Rumpelstiltskin, in fact. The boastfulness of Mr Miller, the greed of the King and the pride of the Queen have all been shown up by this terrible tale. Let their story be a lesson to anybody else who is tempted to be boastful, greedy or proud. As for Mr Rumpelstiltskin, his end was entirely just. He tried to tear a family apart — but ended by tearing himself apart.

My verdict is that the aforesaid Rumpelstiltskin committed suicide. In other words, he took matters into his own hands!

Tell me more

- Only children in Germany heard about Rumpelstilstskin's gruesome end. When the version collected by the brothers Grimm was translated for timid English children the ending was changed to one in which everyone simply laughs at Rumplestiltskin when he gets stuck. In other words, they split their sides instead of him splitting his!

- Rumpelstiltskin was the little man's name in the German version. Elsewhere, different names have been used. None of them any easier to guess . . .

  Tom Tit Tot (much of Britain)
  Trit-a-Trot (Ireland)
  Terrytop, Terrytop-top (Cornwall)
  Whuppity Stoorie (Scotland)
  Ricdin-Ricdon (France)

THEY'RE EVERYWHERE?!

Top Facts 8: Signs, symbols and superstitions

Do you avoid walking under ladders? Touch wood whenever you say what you're planning to do? Refuse to open an umbrella indoors or be the thirteenth person to sit at a table?

If your answer to any of these questions is "yes", then not only are you very superstitious, you're also in a good position to appreciate how lots of details found their way into the fairy tales we know.

Why? Because many of these stories date back to the Middle Ages (500–1500) when the tale-tellers and their listeners were incredibly superstitious, with dozens of signs and symbols that had special meanings. Just how superstitious you can measure from this top ten quiz. So, cross your fingers, and off you go!

1 What's my name?

There's a superstition at the centre of *Rumpelstiltskin*. The little man gets so upset when his name is discovered because, long ago, names were believed to be as much a part of your body as your arms and legs. If somebody knew your name, then it gave them power over you. All a sorcerer or witch had to do to put a curse on you was to call out your name as they recited their magic spell.

(So that's why teachers call the register every day!)

To guard against this happening to newborn babies, their names had to be especially protected until the baby was christened in church. How?

a) The parents didn't choose the name until they were in church and the ceremony had started.

b) The parents chose the name before the ceremony, but didn't tell anybody else what it was.

c) The parents didn't choose the name at all, somebody else did it.

2 Kiss me quick!

We're not told that the Queen's baby is with her when Rumpelstiltskin turns up. That may be for a superstitious reason. What?

a) Babies whose first sight was an ugly face would grow up with ugly faces.

b) Babies would grow up to act like the first person to kiss them.

c) Babies whose cradles were rocked by a little man wouldn't grow up at all.

3 Talking in riddles

Villains in fairy tales often make the hero/heroine solve riddles. But why don't they ask really hard questions instead, like the sort you get for maths homework? Partly because of a superstition about riddles. What was it?

a) Speaking in riddles would confuse any listening evil spirits.

b) Being able to solve riddles was a

sign that you were bewitched.

c) Riddles were secret messages from the Devil.

4 Gimme gold!

Gold turns up in dozens of fairy tales. It's spun out of straw, and eggs made of it are laid by clever geese. That's because gold is valuable. But why should lots of heroines be described as having golden hair? What's that a sign of?

a) They'd be worth a lot of money if they were sold.

b) They were like the sun, always bright and cheerful.

c) They were as good as gold.

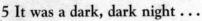

5 It was a dark, dark night . . .

Telling listeners that your story was set in a forest or wood didn't just conjure up for them pictures of a place that was dark and gloomy. It made their hair stand on end by reminding them at once of a common superstition about the dark. What was it?

a) At night trees became alive. They sprouted legs and their branches turned into arms that strangled any humans they met.

b) At night evil air rose from the ground and floated around, poisoning the atmosphere.

c) At night the spirits of the dead roamed the earth looking for new bodies to live in.

6 Dem bones

Bones break into fairy stories pretty often. No self-respecting giant, for instance, would be happy until he'd crunched and munched his way through every one of his victim's bones. As the famous rhyme goes: "Be he alive, or be he dead, I'll grind his bones to make my bread." What superstition made bone-eating an essential part of a giant's diet?

a) Because bones were hard and strong, eating them would make you hard and strong as well.

b) Carrying the bones of somebody who'd died of a nasty disease protected you from catching the same disease.

c) When somebody died, part of them lived on in their bones.

7 Fire!

Listeners would have given a satisfied nod when they heard what happened to the witch in *Hansel and Gretel*. Why?

a) Fire was thought to be a protection against witches and evil spirits.

b) People believed that the walls of an oven could soak up any evil spirits hiding in what was being cooked.

c) Brothers and sisters were believed to have special powers when they tried to help each other instead of arguing.

8 Take one frog three times a day before meals

If you were a fairy tale prince and annoyed a witch, what

would she turn you into? More often than not, a frog. Hearing this, superstitious listeners to the story would suspect at once that you were really a goodie in disguise. Why?

a) Because frog-spawn was thought to be able to stop bleeding.

b) Because frogs were thought to be able to cure diseases like whooping cough.

c) Because the rough skin of frogs was thought to be able to cure warts.

9 It's all done by mirrors

In *Snow White* the wicked Queen famously asks her mirror questions about who is the fairest of them all – and gets answers! What common superstition made listeners think this was perfectly possible?

a) A bewitched mirror could reflect thoughts as well as faces, and so could put ideas into your head.

b) Mirrors could be used by fortune-tellers to make predictions.

c) An evil spirit could control a mirror so that its reflection wasn't seen when it was in the room.

10 Where wolves were werewolves

The most famous wolf in fiction must be the one on the cover of this book – the wolf that gave *Little Red Riding Hood* a run for her money. As you'll see in Story 4, he was a wolf with a crafty line in chat. So could he have started out as a werewolf – a human who could turn into a wolf?

a) No. People in the Middle Ages didn't believe in werewolves.
b) Maybe. Some people believed in werewolves, but not many.
c) Definitely. Almost everybody believed in werewolves – because a group of church leaders said they really existed!

Answers:

1b) The baby's name was chosen, but only close relatives were told what it was. Even then, the name wasn't used before the christening. Whenever Mum and Dad wanted to coo in their baby's ear, they would fool any evil spirits that were listening in by using a different name: a *nickname*. Some families were even more cautious. Dad would choose the name, but not tell anybody else what it was – no, not even the baby's mum!

2b) So it was important to make sure all the nice relatives were invited round first, and all the miserable ones left until last!

3c) The Devil was said to speak in riddles, and so anybody who could solve them could beat him at his own game. Besides, a hero who could solve riddles would have impressed the common listener much more than one who could trot out the answers to hard maths questions. Why? Because to do maths you had to be educated, and Mr and Mrs Peasant weren't. But solving a riddle was different. That needed *intelligence* and was a sure sign that the hero/heroine was special, because intelligence was a gift from God.

4c) The reason gold is valuable is that it doesn't go rusty or mouldy. It's always pure and keeps its beauty. So giving a heroine fair or golden hair is a sign that she's "as good as gold"; a lovely person, both in appearance and how she behaves. Maybe *that's* why they're called fair-y tales!

5b) When the sun came up and the light returned, this evil air went back to where it came from. So in forests and woods, where the sun couldn't reach, they naturally thought the evil air was able to float around all the time.

6c), and possibly **b)** as well. Because a person's

skeleton was still rattling around when everything else had rotted away, bones were thought to hold some left-overs of their owner's life. (For instance, in a story called *The Singing Bone*, when a murdered man's bone is used to make the frame of a harp its first act is to sing out the name of the murderer!) So using bones, especially those of a brave enemy you'd beaten, gained you his courage as well. Favourite bone of the lot was the skull, which was usually turned upside down and used as a cup!

Though there's no suggestion that giants needed protection from any nasty diseases, people did think that the bones of the dead could help. Try a couple for yourselves. If you have to keep dashing to the loo, the answer is a glass of red wine with powdered bones. And for a sore big toe (gout) there's supposed to be nothing finer than covering it with a splodge of earth and shin-bone scrapings!

7a) What you might call a sure-fire protection, in fact. Because fire can destroy anything, evil spirits were thought to be frightened to cross its path. Newborn babies, for instance, were protected against evil spirits by having their cradles surrounded by a ring of candles. So, for Hansel and Gretel to burn the witch to death was to guarantee that she'd stay dead because every part of her, including her bones (see **6**) would be gone!

8a), b) and **c)** The way to treat a cut was to bind it up with strips of cloth that had been soaked in frog-spawn three days before a new moon. At least that was easy on the frog. In order to cure whooping cough the frog had to be dead. It was then hung in a box round the patient's neck and, as its body decayed, the cough was supposed to disappear. Getting rid of warts was the worst job of all. The frog had to be rubbed across them, then pinned on a thorn tree to die. No wonder fairy-tale frogs jumped for joy when they were turned back into princes again!

9b) In this way, mirrors were just like crystal balls. Fortune-tellers would gaze into a mirror and – they said – would see answers to questions they'd been asked. Many other mirror superstitions exist. Girls, try this one on Hallowe'en. After lighting two candles, stand in front of a mirror brushing your hair and eating an apple. You'll see the face of your future husband looking over your shoulder! (Either that or you'll mess up your hair, get indigestion and burn the house down).

10c) Most people believed in werewolves. They were supposed to roam around at night eating babies and, if they were really starving, might even go in for some grave-robbing and eat a corpse or two. (Maybe this was how games of "corpse and robbers" began!) Do your eyebrows meet in the middle? In Iceland, Denmark and Germany, you'd have been suspected of being a werewolf!

Story 7: Snowdrop

In the number 7 spot is the story of Snowdrop. Stories like it have been found in Europe, Asia and Africa: the European story was published in 1634. The heroine is usually called Snow White nowadays, mainly because that was the name given her in the 1938 Disney screen cartoon version. To begin with, though, she was called Snowdrop . . . and a perfect name it is for the star of this story.

Why? Because a snowdrop is a pure white flower. Its only fault is that it blooms in winter and makes everything around it look dull and dowdy. That's how nature intended it, and the country-wise tellers of this story would have known it well.

But if you're beautiful yourself, and somebody appears who puts you in the shade . . . well, how do you feel?

Jealous? Of course! Murderous? Hopefully, not! But that's what the little story of Snowdrop is about: insane jealousy and attempted murder. Perfect for a cartoon serial!

So here it is, the story of Snowdrop in ten bloodthirsty episodes. It even has a bloody beginning . . .

Sleep tight!

1 It was winter. As a Queen sat sewing at her window, she pricked her finger and three drops of blood fell onto the snow outside.

I WISH I HAD A CHILD WITH A FACE AS WHITE AS SNOW, CHEEKS AS RED AS BLOOD AND HAIR AS BLACK AS THIS EBONY WINDOW.

The Queen's wish was granted. Snowdrop was born and grew up exactly as her mother had wanted. But the Queen wasn't there to see it happen. Even as Snowdrop was born, she had died!

A year later, the King took another wife for his Queen...

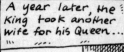

HELLO STEPMOTHER!

MUTTER, MUTTER, MUTTER

The new Queen was a beauty. But was she the number one beauty Queen? She had her own way of finding out.

TELL ME GLASS, TELL ME TRUE! OF ALL THE LADIES IN THE LAND, WHO IS THE FAIREST? TELL ME WHO!

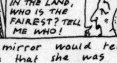

And the mirror would tell the Queen that she was the one...

2 Until, that is, Snowdrop was seven years old. That day when the Queen asked her usual question the mirror answered...

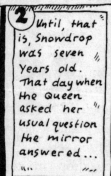

SNOWDROP. SORRY!

YOU'RE CRACKED! TRY AGAIN, I SAY!

BAD LUCK. IT'S STILL SNOWDROP

In a jealous rage, the queen commanded her servant to take Snowdrop out into the forest and kill her.

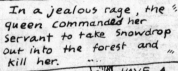

HAVE A HEART!

I WILL! SNOWDROP'S. BRING IT BACK TO ME AS PROOF THAT SHE'S DEAD!

But the servant couldn't bring himself to kill the child. So he let Snowdrop go free and killed a wild boar instead. Cutting out its heart, he delivered it to the Queen.

NOW, SAY I'M HEARTLESS!

Believing the heart to be Snowdrop's, she had it cooked, sprinkled it with a little salt, and ate it. (Now that's what you call an all-consuming jealousy!)

3 Meanwhile, Snowdrop had wandered through the forest and found a house. Inside there were seven of everything. Seven chairs Seven beds Seven dwarves. ...

WHO ARE YOU?

MY NAME'S SNOWDROP. I'M COLD AND HUNGRY AND LOST AND MY STEP-MOTHER WANTS TO KILL ME AND....

After telling them her story, the dwarves took pity on her and agreed that Snowdrop could stay there with them.

4 Back at the palace, the queen checked with her mirror again.

TELL ME GLASS TELL ME TRUE! OF ALL THE LADIES IN THE LAND.... OH YOU KNOW! THE USUAL!

AND IT'S THE USUAL ANSWER I'M AFRAID. SNOWDROP.

WHAT! WHERE IS SHE?

IN A HOUSE BEYOND THE HILLS. WITH SEVEN LITTLE PEOPLE.

LITTLE PEOPLE EH? THEN SHE SHALL SEE ME SHORTLY!

5 Thus the queen, deciding that if she wanted something done properly she would have to do it herself, disguised herself as a harmless old seller of buttons and laces. Reaching the dwarves' house, she sold Snowdrop a new lace for her tie-up belt. And helped her tie it up...

IT'S TOO TIGHT. I CAN'T BREATHE!

BELT UP!

"Tighter and tighter she pulled, until finally Snowdrop slumped to the ground and didn't move.

Snowdrop lay on the ground apparently dead.

THAT'S THE END OF YOU! EASY SQUEEZY!

"When the dwarves came home and saw what had happened they were grief-stricken — until one of them untied the lace and Snowdrop recovered."

IT MUST HAVE BEEN THE WICKED QUEEN

6 Once again, the Queen consulted her mirror. But once again, she got the same answer and realized Snowdrop hadn't died. Next day she returned to the house in the forest, and this time talked Snowdrop into buying a clasp for her hair. A clasp that she had dipped in poison......

HAIR YOU ARE, MY DEAR!

OW!

Snowdrop lay on the ground apparently dead.

AH WELL HAIR TODAY, GONE TOMORROW!

Once again the dwarves returned home to find Snowdrop seemingly dead — and once more they saved her by pulling the poisened clasp out of her head.

IN FUTURE YOU MUST BE CAREFUL WHO YOU ANSWER THE DOOR TO.

7 When the Queen spoke once more with her mirror, and discovered yet again that Snowdrop was still alive, she decided that enough was enough. Her next idea had to be an absolute pippin. And it was. Dressed as a fruit-seller, she approached the dwarves' house.

HAVE SOME FRUIT DEAR. GOOD FOR YOU.

I'VE BEEN TOLD NOT TO TAKE THINGS FROM STRANGERS. I KEEP GETTING POISONED

THIS ONE'S PERFECT. LOOK I'LL TAKE A BITE MYSELF.

Taking a bite from the half of the apple that she'd left alone, the Queen wiped a trickle of juice from her chin and handed it back.

OH, THAT'S ALL RIGHT THEN. A SNACK WOULD BE A NICE IDEA.

A PEACH OF AN IDEA!

LOOKS LIKE AN APPLE TO ME.

Snowdrop eats...

DEADLY POISONED BIT—

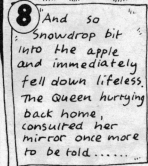

8 And so Snowdrop bit into the apple and immediately fell down lifeless. The Queen hurrying back home, consulted her mirror once more to be told......

THOU QUEEN ARE THE FAIREST OF ALL !

This time, there was nothing the dwarves could do to revive Snowdrop, even though they cried and wailed for three days. But the thought of burying her in the cold ground was too awful. So they placed her in a glass coffin and carried her carefully to the top of a hill where they took turns to watch over it night and day.

THIRD TIME UNLUCKY

9 There, Snowdrop lay until one day a handsome Prince came riding by and fell in love with her. He offered to take her away and give her a better resting-place. But when the coffin was moved, the piece of poisoned apple fell out from Snowdrop's mouth. Waking up, she set eyes on the Prince.....

COR!

CORE!

COR!

AH!

10 Snowdrop and her Prince announced their forthcoming marriage. Being royalty, the Queen was invited. But when she next looked in her mirror....

OK. JUST SAY. IT'S ME ISN'T IT?

ER...NO. NOT ANYMORE.

WHO IS IT? WHO IS IT!

IT'S... OH, YOU KNOW, WHAT'S HER NAME? IT'S ON THE TIP OF MY FRAME....

NOT... SNOWDROP?

THAT'S THE ONE. SHE'S THE ONE GETTING MARRIED Y'KNOW.

Enraged, the Queen went to the wedding —— and was recognized. The whole story came out, and the Queen's punishment was decided. A pair of iron shoes were laid on a furnace and heated until they were red hot. Then, taking no notice of her screams of agony, these shoes were put on the wicked Queen's feet and she was made to dance in them until she dropped dead.

SCREAMMMMMM

SHE'LL BE HOPPING MAD ABOUT THIS!

Tell Me More

- What you might call a sizzling ending! It was left out of many later versions because it was such a gruesome punishment. (The wicked Queen raced hotfoot away from the wedding instead.) But early listeners would have loved it because they'd have seen the Queen as a bit of a witch and burning her feet with red-hot iron shoes was a way of using fire against her.

- Having the little men guard Snowdrop's coffin was in keeping with the times as well. "Watching over the dead" was a common practice. It stopped evil spirits stealing the corpse's soul before it was given a Christian burial. Because the little men decided Snowdrop was too beautiful to be buried, they had to watch over her all the time.

- The little men weren't called Dopey, Sleepy, Grumpy, etc. either. The names were a Disney invention. Usually they weren't named, although the artist John Hassel did so in 1921 – by giving them breeches (like short trousers) with their names on! His choice of names was a bit dodgy, though. They were – Stool, Plate, Bread, Spoon, Fork, Knife and Wine! How did Snowdrop ask them to do anything? "Pass me the bread knife" could have resulted in Knife lobbing Bread across the table!

Top Facts 7: Happy childhoods!

A regular fact of fairy-tale life is that being a child is no fairy tale! *Snowdrop, Hansel and Gretel, Rumpelstiltskin* . . . they're positively littered with children in all sorts of danger. But they're only stories, aren't they? They're not based on real life, are they?

Sort out the truth from the fiction with this top ten test about fairy tale family facts.

1 When the fairy tales were taking shape, people stayed married for ever. There were hardly any stepmothers around. TRUE or FALSE?
FALSE. Stepmothers were very common. Childbirth was a dangerous business, and many women died when their babies were born. Fairy stories that begin with the death of a mother (like *Snowdrop*) are simply being true to life.

It's the same when they say the husband married again soon after. Finding a replacement mother for his children would have been important for a man.

2 In fairy tales it's always the stepmother who's wicked, not the real mother. TRUE or FALSE?
FALSE. It might be so now, but it wasn't always that way. Story-tellers have changed things over the years. Jacob and Wilhelm Grimm, for instance, didn't like the version of *Hansel and Gretel* they'd heard because it had the children's real mother (and father) packing them off

to die. They didn't want children to see a mother behaving that way. So they changed the story to make her into a stepmother or, sometimes, a mother-in-law. As mothers-in-law were also known as stepmothers, though, the mother-in-law title fell out of use. The wicked stepmother had arrived ... and no story ever stopped to ask why the husband was so thick as to marry such an old boot in the first place!

3 Hansel and Gretel is based on fact. Parents who couldn't afford to feed their children sometimes did take them out and leave them to die.

TRUE or FALSE?

TRUE. Poor parents with more children than they could feed had a terrible problem. In the days before welfare hand-outs and social services, they'd decide that somebody had to go – and it wouldn't be them! Newborn babies were most at risk. They'd be "exposed" – a gentler way of saying that they'd be left out in the open until they either died or grew up and could fend for themselves. Needless to say, not many grew up.

Girls were even worse off. Not only did they cost money while they were growing up, they were expensive to marry off. A bride had to be accompanied by a dowry, paid by the girl's family to her new husband. Abandoning newborn girls was seen as putting off a future expense!

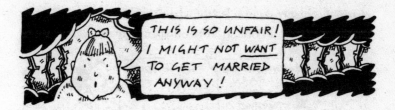

4 You were in even more danger of being taken out and left to die if you were a twin. TRUE or FALSE?

TRUE. And not always because of the cost. Twins were regularly separated at birth, with one being kept and the other abandoned. Why? Because, with their limited medical knowledge, people thought that the husband could only be the father of one of the children – and so the other must be the child of another man or, even worse, the Devil! So the top tip for babies was: don't be a girl twin in a poor family!

5 Fairy stories which show boys and girls being sent away to find their fortune are true to life. That really did happen. TRUE or FALSE?

TRUE for boys, but FALSE for girls. A boy who was too clever (or, maybe, too feeble!) to help his family by working out in the fields could be sent away to be educated – and an educated man, able to read and write, was one who could "earn a fortune".

Girls, on the other hand, stayed at home and worked until they could be married off! And if they never married they remained "spinsters" – women who had nothing else to do but sit at their spinning wheels all day.

6 Parents sometimes promised to give away their children, just like the girl did in Rumpelstiltskin. TRUE or FALSE?

FALSE. Parents did sometimes "promise" their children, but not in the same way. In the Middle Ages, when religious belief was very strong, parents would often vow to have one of their sons trained to be a priest in the church. In this way they were saying "thanks" to God. This was the complete opposite of doing a deal with an evil character like Rumpelstiltskin – that would have been seen as offering a child to the Devil.

7 Stories in which the youngest son wins the day against his elder brothers are fanciful because a young brother didn't have any advantages at all. TRUE or FALSE?

TRUE. The eldest son would inherit everything his father left behind. He would become the new master of the house, and his brothers would have to look up to him. So stories which show the opposite happening really are describing the fairy-tale life a young brother might wish for – because he wouldn't get it any other way!

8 There's plenty of evidence in fairy tales to show that children who stayed at home were expected to work hard and be good. TRUE or FALSE?

TRUE. A very common story type has two children in a family being compared to each other. Stories like *Old Mother Frost*, which the Grimm Brothers told. In this story a beautiful, hard-working girl jumps into a well to recover a spindle she's accidentally dropped. Down below she meets an ugly old woman who asks her to stay and work for her. The girl does so happily, and is rewarded when she leaves by being showered with gold coins.

Of course, after hearing her story, her lazy sister decides to jump down the well too. There she agrees to work for old woman – but lazes around instead. On the day she goes home she's showered with tar! Moral: good children are given presents, bad children get punished.

9 Fairy godmothers are an invention. There never were such people. TRUE or FALSE?

FALSE. Godparents – especially godmothers – were very important people in the life of a child. During the Christian ceremony of baptism (otherwise known as christening) they promised to do all they could to support their godchild. It was almost as if they were joint parents. So having a rich godparent really could help your dreams come true! Fairy godmothers are just the story-teller's version of the ideal godparent.

10 When the stories were written down and pictures added, fairy godmothers were almost always shown as twinkling beauties. TRUE or FALSE?

FALSE. Cinderella's lovely, wand-waving pumpkin-changer is a 20th-century invention. Fairy godmothers weren't always shown as Glamorous Grannies. In the early days of illustrating fairy tales, artists would show them as ugly old bags. For instance, one drew Cinderella's fairy godmother as a stick-carrying old woman with a hooked nose and long, bony fingers, wearing a dark cloak and a tall black pointed hat. Why? Because it showed Cinderella in a better light, as a girl who didn't care what people looked like so long as they were good-hearted.

Story 6: The Little Sea-Maid

Have you got your handkerchiefs ready? Because for this, the story in number 6 position, you're probably going to need them. You see, not every fairy story was given a happy ending, and this one certainly wasn't. It dates from around 1840 and is by Hans Christian Andersen, a story-teller who didn't see any reason at all why the characters in his stories should live happily ever after.

The Little Sea-Maid isn't satisfied with her life; she wants more than nature has given her. Worse, in order to get it, the Sea-Maid makes a deal with a "devil": a Sea-Witch. Some fairy stories allow their heroines to get away with this sort of behaviour, but Andersen showed exactly what he thought by having his heroine end up losing everything.

In fact, the only character who's at all happy at how things work out is the villain of the piece, the Sea-Witch herself.

So get ready to boo and hiss – but hang on to those hankies, because all the boos and hisses in the world won't change the ending . . .

A cautionary tail

They call me the Sea-Witch. Good name, I like it. Not flashy, but it says all there is to say about me.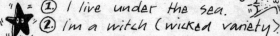

① I live under the sea.
② I'm a witch (wicked variety)

Do a deal with me and you take what you get. I've got no time for sympathy if it goes wrong. In fact, I quite like it. Oh, who am I kidding? I REALLY like it. That's what was so beautifully, wonderfully enjoyable about that idiot Sea-Maid. Pull up a drowned sailor's skull and sit down. I'll tell you all about it.

The merman king, the sea-Maid's father, had six daughters. Nasty little creatures, all of them, but the most unpleasant of them all was number six. She was so pretty and had such a beautifull voice it was enough to make anybody sea-sick.

But being pretty and able to sing wasn't enough for her, I'm very pleased to say! She wasn't satisfied. And it's those who aren't satisfied who keep the likes of me in business.

No the sea-Maid couldn't wait for her fifteenth birthday. Why? Because that's when she would be allowed up to sea-level for the first time. So, when the day came, up she swam. And what was the first thing she clapped eyes on? A human prince.

He was on board a ship — a revolting, horrible thing, like most of them are. (The ship was quite nice, though.) This prince was standard human shape, with two of nearly everything. Ugly as sin if you ask me, but quite handsome if you like that sort of thing. And the Sea-Maid DID like that sort of thing! The little fool fell head-over-tail in love with him!

Well, then a storm blew up and the prince was washed overboard. Of course he was useless in the sea, a complete wet. So wonderful Sea-Maid, the little goody two-fins fishes him out of the water and carries him to the safety of a nearby beach. There he recovered and was found by a human girl — who, much to the Sea-Maid's distress, the prince assumed had been the one who'd saved him!

That's when the silly sea-girl came to visit me in my underwater home. She found it a bit different to the merman king's palace, I can tell you! That's a foul place, all

91

made out of gruesome pink sea shells and the like. My home is quite beautiful. It's surrounded by warm, bubbling mud and completely made out of the bleached bones of dead sailors. Heavenly! And when I let myself in the front door I've got millions of the fattest, yellowest water snakes to keep me company!

I could tell the sea-Maid was terrified. All credit to her though, the little fool plucked up enough courage to swim into my gracious presence.

"I want....." she began.

"I know what you want," I said. "You want to become a human. Right?"

"Yes. So I can marry my prince."

"Well you know what that means. Humans don't marry fish, they eat them. If you want to be a human you'll have to lose that tail and get a couple of legs."

"Can you help me?"

"Yes, I can mix you up a potion that will make your tail tail off."

"And give me two legs?"

"Of course. And they won't be any old rubbish. You'll be able to dance like no human has danced before. But—"

I gave it to her straight—"it will feel like you're dancing on sharp knives. Whenever you do, your feet will bleed."

The little fool looked uncertain. For a minute I thought I'd gone too far, and I wasn't going to get what I was after. But then she said the magic words.

"Say no more," she said. "I'll pay whatever it costs."

"Say no more!" I cackled. "That is what it costs!"

Yes, the price she had to pay for my special tail-removing potion was her tongue. The deal was done. I used some of my best black blood to make her potion, then carefully snipped out that dainty little tongue. Lovely!

So, up to the surface swam dear dumb little Sea-Maid where she swallowed her potion. It hurt, of course. Well, you know what they say: "no gain without pain". But then what's the agony of feeling that you're being sliced through by a double edged sword when at the end of it you've lost your tail and gained a couple of legs? Especially when she woke up—silly me, I forgot to mention that the pain would be so agonising she'd probably faint — and her prince was there in front of her. The conversation was a bit one-sided of course.

"Hello!" said the prince.

Silence.

"What's the matter, cat got your tongue?"

Silence

"Never mind. I like a quiet life. How about a dance?"

So the Sea-Maid danced and did it beautifully. Her bleeding feet left a nasty mess on the carpet, of course, but I did warn her — and the prince didn't seem to mind.

Finally my dim-wit Sea-Maid discovered what should have been obvious from the very beginning — that not having a voice made it impossible to blow her own trumpet.

"I really like you," the prince told her one day, "but I can't marry you. You see, I plan to marry another: the girl who saved me from drowning."

He didn't mean the Sea-Maid, though. He meant the girl he'd first seen after he'd come round on the beach. The twerp didn't have a clue that it was Sea-Maid who'd really pulled him out — and without a voice she couldn't tell him! Talk about miserable!

So the prince got married. As for Sea-Maid, she was in for another change — from mermaid to "bridesmaid! Yes, she had to stand by and watch her love marry another.

I wasn't finished with the family yet, though. Her sisters had seen everything and felt terribly for her. So now they came down to my little home to plead with me.

"Isn't there something you can do to change her back into a mermaid again?"

That's the trouble with some people. Keen and eager to go for what they want, then when it all goes wrong they want to go back and start again. Sorry, but it's not that easy.

"You know what the rules say," I hissed. "Them that change into a human do so at their own risk. If the man your sister loves marries another, that's it. At daybreak the morning after, she turns into sea foam."

"Foam? You mean she'll die?"

Stupid girls! "She won't be bubbling with life, that's for sure!" I cackled.

They promptly burst into tears. I don't know, some mermaids have no sense of humour. Well, what could a poor sea-witch do but try to help? Besides, they too had something I wanted — their hair. I don't know what shampoo sea-maids use but they have really nice hair, growing right down to their waist. What a waste! I'd always thought it would look much better on me.

95

"Let me cut off all your hair," I said. "And I'll give you the answer."

They agreed of course, as I knew they would. Sisterly love, they call it. Utter stupidity, I call it.

"So what's the answer, then?" they snapped.

Losing one's hair does make one speak very baldly, I've found.

I gave them a knife. "Easy. Get your sister to kill the prince before daybreak. Tell her she must plunge the knife into him and let his blood drip on her feet. Do that, and she will return to what she was before."

So, off they went and told the Sea-Maid what she had to do. But did she do it? No she did not.

As the sun was coming up, she crept into the prince's bedroom. She raised the knife..... only to realize that she couldn't do it. Her love for him was too great to kill him. Bah! Her brain was too small, if you ask me.

So instead of throwing the knife at him, she threw it into the sea. Well, that was that. Before you could say "Bad morning!" dawn had broken. The pathetic Sea-Maid threw herself into the sea. It was all over very quickly. She couldn't have felt any pain. One moment she was a girl, the next she'd died and turned to foam.

Oh, come on! Stop that sniffing! I did warn you it was a sad story, didn't I?

Look on the bright side. There was one winner. Yes, little old me! Now I've got everything a sea-witch could want: a lovely voice; masses of beautiful hair; and plenty of dead sea-maid foam to wash it in.

Gorgeous, that's what I am.

Maybe I'll pop up and see that princey wincey myself!

Tell me more

- The tough ending tells you a lot about Hans Christian Andersen. He believed that everybody and everything had a set place in the world. Those who defied that "law", and tried to change what had been planned for them in life, were taking a mighty risk.
- Like other endings, it's been changed by different tale-tellers so that children hearing it wouldn't be upset at the end. Check out the Disney cartoon version, *The Little Mermaid*. In that, the sea-maid gets her wish and marries the prince. Disgusting!

Top Facts 6: Wicked witches

Those who say that fairy stories aren't true to life have got it all wrong. Everybody knows it's easier to be bad than good – especially if you think that, by being bad, you'll get what you really really want. It's called temptation! That's what the Sea-Maid couldn't resist.

Where fairy tales were concerned, witches were part of the Devil's wicked gang. Heroes and heroines were supposed to fight against them, not make deals with them. If they did, they usually lived to regret it.

But how did witches get to be in the tales at all? Did people really believe they existed? They certainly did. This was especially so in Europe in the infamous "witch-hunting" years of 1450–1650, the period just before many of the classic fairy tales were written down. And it didn't take much to be suspected of being a witch . . .

SO THERE I WAS, HALF WAY THROUGH THE CAT FLAP AND THE SPELL WORE OFF !

1 Do you have a pet cat? A black one, maybe? Not a good idea. Witches were able to turn themselves into cats, that was a well-known fact. In 1718 a Scot named William Montgomery attacked a crowd of cats with an axe, saying they'd turned up outside his house night after night and talked to each other – in English! He also claimed to have killed two and injured some of the others. Next day, he heard that two old women in the area had been found dead in their beds and saw another walking around with a cut leg!

2 No cat? That doesn't mean you're safe. Maybe you have a different sort of pet? A mouse, a dog, a rabbit or a hare? Still not a good idea. Witches were suspected of being able to turn themselves into any of these as well (not to mention foxes, ferrets, weasels and a whole zoo of other animals). In Great Britain and Ireland the favourite animal shape for a witch was supposed to be a hare. One nutty Scots witch, named Isobel Gowdie, admitted this in 1662 and even revealed part of the rhyme she used:

> I SHALL GO INTO A HARE,
> WITH SORROW AND SUCH
> AND MANY A CARE
> I SHALL GO IN THE DEVIL'S
> NAME
> AYWHILE I COME HOME AGAIN...

Do not try this at home! If it works, you'd need another rhyme to change back again!

3 Afraid of the dark and prefer to find your way to bed by candlelight? Dodgy. In 1490 a woman named Johanna Benet was accused of attempted murder by witchcraft. What was she supposed to have done? Named a candle after a man so that, as the candle burned down he got weaker and weaker until ... good-night!

> I'VE GOT A BLAZING HEAD-ACHE AND I'M GETTING LIGHTER..!

4 Fond of scrambled egg for breakfast? Suspicious. In 1583 a woman known only to her neighbours as Mother Gabley was supposed to have caused 14 men to be drowned. How? By putting eggs into a bucket of water and mashing them up.

5 Wear a pair of gloves to keep out the cold? Oh, dear. In 1619 Joan Flower and her two daughters were hanged for murdering a young aristocrat, Lord Rosse, with one of his gloves! Having stolen it from him, they'd rubbed it against Mrs Flower's black cat, dipped it in boiling water, jabbed holes in it and finally buried it. Lord Rosse duly fell ill and died.

6 Given pocket-money every week? Be careful! The Lee Penny, a penny with a red triangular stone set in the back of it, was owned by a north of England family named Lockheart. In 1645, after it was given the credit for curing an outbreak of plague in Newcastle, the then owner, Sir James Lockheart, was investigated . . . but let off with a warning because the stone had only ever done good and no spells were spoken when it was waved around!

7 Like to wear the latest trainers? Check where they've been. Shoes were thought to contain something of their owner – and not just the smell of their feet! To acquire one from somebody gave you power over them. In 1644 one of the charges against a male witch named Patrick Malcolm was that he tried to bring a woman under his spell by talking her into giving him her left shoe. (The jury must have known at once that wasn't right!)

8 Is your room a tip? Great, keep it that way! Witches and brooms go together, of course, but household dust also used to be superstitiously linked with money. In 1323 an Irish woman named Alice Kyteler was accused of trying to rob her neighbours. How? By sweeping their front doorsteps!

9 Is it blowing a gale outside? Then stay indoors! Witches were supposed to enjoy storms and be able to start them at will. Not that it always worked. In 1590, a coven of Scots witches tried to wreck the ship carrying James VI back home. Their spell was gruesome – as they chanted they tied bits of a dead

man's body to a cat and threw it into the sea to drown! The result: one dead cat and a gentle breeze.

10 Still got your collections of dolls or action men figures? Ditch them at once! Doing nasty things to models of people they don't like is something witches have always been thought able to do – not just in the 15th century but in the 20th too. On 14 December 1900, for instance, a model of William McKinley, the

President of the USA, was poked with pins and set alight outside the American Embassy in London. (Did McKinley start to suffer from pins and needles or heartburn? It's not known. But he was assassinated a year later!)

Story 5: Beauty and the Beast

Would you agree to go and live with somebody you'd never met and didn't think you could possibly love?

No? Let's change the question slightly, then. Would you agree to go and live with somebody you'd never met if the alternative was that somebody you really did love, like your fantastic father, would have to die . . .

Not so sure, now? Good for you. Let's make the question even harder, then. Would you still go ahead if the person you'd have to live with wasn't human – but a talking pig, say, or a goat, or a monkey? Or, even worse, a huge slobbering beast that is uglier than you could possibly imagine?

No way? Not in a million years?

Understandable – but such a pity about your poor beloved father, though. Let's hope his death will be quick, and that he won't blame you for not saving him when you had the chance . . .

This is the dilemma posed by the classic story in number 5 position, Beauty and the Beast. It was written by two French women. Gabrielle-Suzanne Villeneuve, a nobleman's daughter, wrote a mega-version in 1740. This was later trimmed down by Jeanne-Marie Beaumont, a teacher who wrote a lot about how young ladies needed to work hard and be modest if they were to be happy.

It's a story of love. Not the stomach-churning "Oooh, I love him to bits and I'll stay with him for ever ... unless I get fed up with him or somebody else comes along, of course" sort of romances you read about every day in the papers.

No, this is real love. The kind that makes a person be prepared to give up everything. Now, that would make front-page news ...

OLDEN TYMES

The events of yesterday, printed today!

The Wedding of the Year

BEAUTY AND BEAST TO WED

Love turns tragedy to triumph

Verily, it promises to be the marriage of the year and your favoured news-sheet has made ready with the story you won't want to miss. It's the most magical tale of Beauty

SHE'LL MAKE A BEAUTY—FUL BRIDE!

and the Beast, wherein love conquered all. Moreover, it commences today, only in your golden *Olden Tymes!*

DAY 1: THOU ART A LITTLE BEAUTY!

A truly startling stunner, Beauty started stunning from her earliest days. She was the youngest in a family of six, having three strong brothers and two sisters who were fair of face. As her proud papa related to our news-gatherer: "She wert a considerable stunner from the very outset. It was for that reason I named her Beauty."

And, truly, his daughter was not merely a beauty – she was possessed of a fine quantity of brains as well. While her sisters travelled far and wide, scouring the land for the most handsome of hunks, little Beauty preferred nothing more than the company of a good book. Marriage was not in her thoughts.

OH! ....WHAT A BEAUTY !!! ALL THIS AND BRAINS TOO!

Then, one day, a letter arrived for her father:

Dear Sir,
Thou remember the ship thou sank all thy money in? Well, — we think it's been sunk. Trusting that these tidings won't make you feel too down,
U. R. Broke

BEAUTY STAYS CHEERFUL..
... BUT GETS AN EARFUL !

It was a terrible time. Thus impoverished, the family moved to a small house in the countryside.

But did Beauty wail and weep? Verily, she did not. She resolved instead to help her dear papa by rising at four o'clock every morn to cook and clean for the household. As for her selfish and useless sisters, they did nothing but laze about, moaning and groaning. Then, one day, another letter arrived:

Dear Sir,
Utmost congratulations ! Further to my incompetent brother's earlier letter, this is to inform you that your ship has come in ! You're rolling in it !
Your obedient (and hopefully well-rewarded servant,
U. R. Knot - Broke

The family celebrated grandly! Beauty's scrounging sisters now made merriest of all. Before their father went away they compiled a shopping list of top designer dresses they wanted him to bring back for them. And Beauty? All she requested was a rose, because none grew in their part of the country.

SELFISH SISTERS SNEER AT BEAUTY'S FLOWERY REQUEST

WHAT THEY SAID:

"Blitz the shops, Pop! Spend, spend, spend – on us! We want to look sensationally sensational and stunningly stunning!" – the sisters.

 "Just a rose, please. That's all I'd like, Daddy" – Beauty.

"A sweet rose – just like you, petal" – Beauty's tearful dad as he set off.

"Yuk!" – the sisters.

Part 2 tomorrow, only in your golden *Olden Tymes!*

OLDEN TYMES
The events of yesterday, printed today!

BEAUTY AND BEAST TO WED
Love turns tragedy to triumph

DAY 2: A MEETING IS ARRANGED

So the happy merchant went about his business – unfortunately leaving his poor home just after another letter arrived:

Dear Sir,

Oops! My second brother got it wrong and my first brother got it right. Your finances are still rock-bottom. Rather like your ship, really.

Yours faithfully,
U. R. Still-Broke

Worse was to come. On his way home, Beauty's papa became lost in a dark and sullen wood – wherein suddenly he espied through the trees a fabulous million pound mansion. In fear and trepidation he approached it, hoping that the owner might afford him hospitality, be it no more than a cup of tea and a ham roll.

And lo! As he drew near, the front door swung open! In the merchant

"SUPER! A SUMPTUOUS SUPPER"
DECLARES A DELIGHTED DAD!

ventured, to find nothing less than an exceeding slap-up meal and luxurious bedchamber awaiting him. So he ate his fill and had a good night's kip – yet all without once encountering the master of the mansion, not even when he woke on the morrow. What he did espy, though, was a bunch of rampant roses growing in the garden.

BEAUTY'S DAD WAKES UP
TO A ROSY OUTLOOK!

"Verily, I remembered at once my Beauty's request of me," he told our news-gatherer. "So I went out and nicked one ... I mean picked one. Well, both really."

But what happened thereafter was the matter of nightmares.

"At once I heard a terrible roar and saw, lumbering towards me, the beastliest beast ever!"

It was a Beast in no mood for idle chatter. "What dost thou think thou art doing, stealing my roses? Say your prayers, ungrateful man! And then I will most certainly kill you."

The merchant grovelled, saying he'd only taken it for one of his daughters. "Grrr-ovelling will serve thee a fat lot of good," said Beast. "But, I have a mind to spare you – on one condition. I will give thee much money. In return thou must promise to come back here in three months and suffer at my hands. Unless . . ."

"Unless?" said the merchant, hopefully.

"Unless one of thy daughters offers from the goodness of her heart to come back and suffer on your behalf!"

So the merchant returned home bearing the Beast's money and his rose. In a trice Beauty's sisters grabbed the money. But no sooner had the merchant given Beauty her rose than he broke down in tears.

"WAS IT SOMETHING I SAID?" ASKS A BEWILDERED BEAUTY!

After hearing his sorry tale, Beauty's three brothers said that they would straightway go to Beast's palace and give him a good duffing-up; but their father dissuaded them saying they'd have no chance against Beast. Therewith, Beauty at once proclaimed that she would go with her father, and that he couldn't stop her so there. As for the two sisters, they were greatly chuffed at this idea though they tried not to show it.

WHAT THEY SAID:

"That blooming rose is going to be the death of me!' – Beauty's dad:

"It is all my fault!" – Beauty

"*She's got something right for once*" – the sisters

Part 3 tomorrow, only in your golden *Olden Tymes*!

OLDEN TYMES
The events of yesterday, printed today!

BEAUTY AND BEAST TO WED
Love turns tragedy to triumph

DAY 3: LIVING TOGETHER
And so Beauty went to live with the dreadful Beast in his magnificent mansion deep in the solemn woods. How didst they get on together? Your *Olden Tymes* news-gatherer quizzes the happy couple!

Q: Was it love at first sight?
BEAUTY: No. I was sore afraid of even meeting him, for I had no doubt that he planned to eat me. Even when I saw the

chamber that had been prepared for me, and the gracious dinner table that was laid for me, I still trembled with fear. And when he asked from the shadows if he might join me at my table, I nearly died. But I summoned all my courage and agreed . . .

BEAST: That I was indeed truly ugly.

BEAUTY: But with a good heart. In spite of your ugliness, that I could tell.

Q: So why did you stay, Beauty?

BEAUTY: Because I had given my promise, and I could not break it. And besides, gruesome though Beast was to look at, his manners were those of a gentleman.

Q: Beauty, every reader wants to know this. When did Beast poppest the question?

BEAUTY: Ask me to marry him, you mean? Three months after I moved in.

Q: And how didst thou feel?

BEAST: She nearly fainted. Who could blame her? Apart from being called Mrs B. Beast, just think of how the wedding photographs would have turned out! But, even with her knees knocking for fear that I would eat her, she turned me down in the most gracious style. "I will always be your friend," she said, "but I do not love you."

BEAUTY REFUSES A BEASTLY PROPOSAL!

BEAUTY: He was loathe to take no for an answer, however. Every night he would ask me to be his wife, saying that he loved me. Every night I refused him.

Q: So you arranged a trial separation?

BEAUTY: Yes. But not because I wanted to bid him farewell. The problem was the Beast had furnished my room with a magic mirror. In it I could see my father, all sad and unhappy without me. So I begged Beast to let me pay him a visit. Just for a week.

BEAUTY REFLECTS ON HER DADDY'S MISERY!

BEAST: A week, and no longer. She promised to come back after that. I couldn't believe that she would.

BEAUTY: I did mean to. But ... well ... when I got home ...

WHAT THEY SAID:

"Oh, father!" – Beauty.

"Oh, Beauty!" – Father.

"Oh, no!" – the sisters.

Part 4 tomorrow, only in your golden *Olden Tymes*!

OLDEN TYMES
The events of yesterday, printed today!

BEAUTY AND BEAST TO WED
Love turns tragedy to triumph

DAY 4: TRIAL SEPARATION

Beauty's sisters take up the story.

"Natch, we were well gutted when Beauty returnest home. We'd had it all our own way, thou see, spending all Daddy's loot for him. Then along comes old smarmy knickers and spoils it all."

"But we were sore crafty. When the little baggage revealed that she'd promised to go back to Slobberchops the Beast after a week, we thought it could be a smart move to prevail on her to tarry with us for longer . . ."

"For it was our fervent desire that Beast, greatly angered at our smarmy sister for breaking her promise, would thus welcome her eventual return with open arms – and sharp claws! Not to put too fine a point on it, we hoped he'd rip her to bits and eat her raw!"

So the wicked sisters pretended to be overjoyed at Beauty's return. For the whole week they showed her the utmost kindness. Then, when the time came for Beauty to return to Beast they wailed and cried enough to fill a bucket.

And so, her heart wrenched at the thought of making her sisters unhappy, Beauty agreed to stay longer . . .

BEAUTY AGREES TO HER SISTERS' PLEAS!

WHAT THEY SAID:

"Don't go, Beauty! Don't leave us! We'll miss you like a hole in the head . . . we mean, a whole lot" – the sisters.

"All right. I'll stay for another week" – Beauty.

"Another week! That'll make me feel more than weak . . ." – Beast.

Final Part tomorrow, only in your golden *Olden Tymes*!

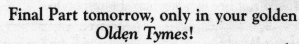

OLDEN TYMES
The events of yesterday, printed today!

BEAUTY AND BEAST TO WED
Love turns tragedy to triumph

DAY 5: LOVE AT LAST!

And so, fair Beauty was tricked into breaking her promise to Beast. She was sore undecided, though, as these previously unpublished letters to the Predicament Page of your very own *Olden Tymes* reveals . . .

Dearest Auntie Agony,

My heart is torn asunder with doubt. I've been living with a revolting ugly beast for three months but am presently visiting my dear father and brothers and sisters. They will be heartbroken to see me leave them, as I will be to go, but the beast says he'll die if I don't return to him. He's a good beast in spite of his ugliness. What dost thou think I should do?

Yours in great doubt and distress,
Beauty

P.S. The beast is rolling in it.

As usual, our straight-conversing Auntie Agony minced not her words when she responded!

Dearest Beauty,

Beast's behaviour, I am afeared, is absolutely typical. Claiming that he'll die if you don't return — taradiddle and turnips! Men try this trick all the time, the fools. Women of today simply won't fall for it any longer. Resist this brazen Beast, that's my advice.

Yours with utmost certainty,
Auntie Agony

P.S. Frankly, I cannot understand why you're even contemplating a return to somebody with such disgusting habits. Rolling in it, you say? Ugh! He must smell awful.

Fortunately, this forthright reply was held up in the post. (Auntie Agony, by the by, is no longer in our employ.) Had Beauty received it, she might have acted differently – and at tragic cost.

As it was she dreamt that Beast, in the belief that she had determined not to return to him, was dying of a broken heart. Unable to stop herself, she set off on a mercy dash back to the palace. She found him in the garden, weak and near to death.

"The minute I saw him lying there, and felt the grief surge in my own heart, I knew I loved him for what he was," said Beauty. "Ugly, indeed. Dim, verily. But a beast who was true and honest. He was the only beast for me."

There and then, she bent down saying, "You must not die. You must live, to be my husband. I *will* marry you. I will be your wife. I will be the mother of your baby beasts and delight at the pitter-patter of their tiny paws!'

After saying which, Beauty tenderly kissed Beast on his wet and glossy snout.

Talkest thou about a terrific transformation! Before her amazed gaze, Beast immediately became a handsome hunk of a prince. In explanation,

COR! WHAT A HANDSOME BEAST!

unless a pure and beautiful girl, caring not for his appearance but recognizing his inner goodness, should come along and agree to getting spliced. And this, Beauty had done!

So, readers, the marriage of the year takes place today. Beauty's family will be there in force – except for two. Her scumbag sisters. Their hardness of heart was rewarded by the rest of their bodies being also hardened. They are to spend their days as statues, standing at the gates of the palace and beholding their sister's happiness for ever more.

the prince recounted how he had been enchanted by a wicked witch. He had been destined to remain thus

WHAT THEY SAID:

"Turned into statues? Stone me!" – *the sisters.*

Tell me more

- Don't fall into the trap of thinking this was just seen as a heart-warming tale. To its earliest listeners it was much more than that – especially to the girls who heard it! Why? Because what they saw in it was. . .

  a) Beauty – the perfect woman, beautiful both inside and out (just like them!) And ...

  b) Beast – the *typical* eating, drinking, belching, swearing, pig-ignorant men they'd been stuck with!! What the story did was bring some hope into their miserable lives: hope that, by kindness and patience, they'd be able to turn their badly-behaved husbands into something resembling human beings!

- In the different versions, Beast was rarely described. Why? Because by *not* describing him, the creature's appearance was left to the reader's own imagination. That way, every reader was guaranteed to come up with the most ghastly picture possible – for them. One of the few descriptions was given by the French writer Madame D'Aulnoy. When Beast first confronts Beauty's father she says that he had "a trunk like an elephant's . . . which he placed on the merchant's neck . . ."

- When the cartoon film version of *Beauty and the Beast* was made in 1996, Beast had to be shown of course so the artists made Beast look like a buffalo. They also gave him quite a princely outfit to wear. Unfortunately, this made him look fairly dashing in a beastly sort of way. When Beauty's kiss turned him back into a human prince, children in the audience were really disappointed – they preferred Beast!

Top Facts 5: Happily ever after!

Nowadays people dream of winning the lottery, but in the Middle Ages, when many fairy tales were taking shape, boys and girls had a different dream; about getting married!

There were two reasons for this – and, typically, they were both good for the boys and rotten for the girls.

One As most men worked on the land, children could be a big help. Children didn't have to go to school (hurrah!) so they could work hard for you instead (boo!). And, so long as you didn't kill them off with all the work, they'd still be around to look after you when you were old. The problem was that to have children without being married was seen as a disgrace. So a wife was what a man needed . . .

Two . . . And preferably a wife with plenty of money! The other attraction about marriage was that it gave a man a chance to become a lot wealthier. A boy would hope to marry a girl from a rich family because she'd have to bring a lot of money with her as part of the deal. So what were the advantages for a girl? That's the mouldy part – quite often there weren't any advantages! As a girl, you cost money to keep so your father would want you off his hands as soon as possible. If you weren't married or at the very least engaged by the time you were 15, people thought there was something wrong with you! Even worse, because your parents "owned" you they could tell you to marry somebody they'd chosen. (Even somebody as old as your grandad!) You had no say in it.

So a girl's dream was not so much that she'd get married, but that she'd marry somebody wonderful, not a big bruiser with a pot-belly and smelly armpits. Somebody who was worthy of her . . .

This is why, in fairy tales, boys are always having to prove themselves good enough for the girl, and on the odd occasion, girls have to prove that they're good enough for the boy.

How? By facing challenges like those in this quiz. They're all to be found in stories collected by the Brothers Grimm. Look them up – but only after you've checked your score and found out if you have what it takes to be a fairy-tale hero/heroine!

Challenge 1 You can't decide who to marry out of three candidates. What do you get them to do?
a) Eat cheese.
b) Walk in a straight line.
c) Say "the rain in Spain stays mainly on the plain".

Challenge 2 An ugly creature helps you recover something valuable. In return you promise to be the creature's playmate if ever you're asked. Lo and behold, the creature turns up at your front door. You tell it to go away. TRUE or FALSE?

Challenge 3 The one you love has been imprisoned in a tower by a witch. How much are you prepared to sacrifice in order to win the day?
a) Your right arm.
b) Your money.
c) Your eyesight.

Challenge 4 Before you can get permission to marry you have to agree that, if your loved one dies before you, you'll be buried alive at the same time! Do you agree – YES or NO?

Challenge 5 Your true love runs off with somebody else. How do you win them back?
a) By fighting a giant.
b) By turning yourself into a flower.
c) By carrying out a daring rescue.

Challenge 6 You're royalty but, on your way to your wedding with another royal your servant tricks you into changing places. Do you tell – YES or NO?

Challenge 7 You're a king who wants to marry a princess. But she's pretty choosy. Whenever somebody turns up to see her she makes fun of them, saying things like: "He's as fat as a wine tub," or, "he's as pale as death." How do you win her heart?

a) By dressing as a beggar.
b) By dressing as a soldier.
c) By dressing as the king you are.

Challenge 8 The one who loves you has a way of making gold coins, but your mother is a witch and she wants you to steal the secret and use it yourselves. Do you AGREE to steal the secret or do you REFUSE?

Challenge 9 You're a prince who's been trapped in an iron stove by a witch! One day a princess comes by. What do you have to talk her into doing so that you can be freed?
a) Bringing a sack of coal and lighting the stove.
b) Bringing a scouring brush and cleaning the stove.
c) Bringing a knife and cutting a hole in the stove.

Challenge 10 You're a lovely girl who gets a job at a queen's palace. "Spin me thread from this flax," says the Queen, showing you a small mountain of the stuff, "and you can marry my son, the Prince!" You fancy the Prince, but hate spinning. Do you AGREE, but don't do it, or REFUSE, but do it anyway?

Answers:

1a) In *The Bride Choosing* a man can't decide which of three girls to marry – so he asks them to eat a piece of cheese and chooses the one who eats hers most carefully.

THAT'S A RELIEF. I THOUGHT THE SMELL WAS COMING FROM YOUR FEET!

2 TRUE It happens in some versions of *The Frog Prince*, in which a frog helps a princess recover a valuable golden ball she's dropped down a well. When the frog turns up to claim her friendship, she refuses to let him in. It's her father, the King, who makes her (showing that girls had no say in the matter!). With much grumbling the princess has to let the frog sleep on her pillow (or, in some versions of the story, let it jump *into* bed with her) and give it a big sloppy kiss before it turns into a prince.

3c) It's the story of Rapunzel who, imprisoned in a tower by a witch, lets down her hair to let her fairy-tale prince climb up to her. When the witch finds out, she banishes Rapunzel to the desert and blinds the Prince. He wanders around until the day Rapunzel finds him, drips two of her tears into his eyes, and restores his sight.

4 YES . . . but it's a bad decision. The story is called the *Three Snake Leaves*. In it, a princess insists that she'll only marry a man who loves her so much that he's prepared to be buried with her if she dies first. The hero does – and so does she! – only for the hero to kill three snakes in the tomb and bring her back to life. Unfortunately she's a changed person and no longer loves the hero. It all ends in tears as she helps have him drowned, by being sent to sea in a ship riddled with holes!

5b) The story is *Roland* and it's an odd one. The heroine loses Roland when he runs off with another woman. She turns herself into a flower and is picked by a shepherd. She turns back into a girl . . . but doesn't marry the shepherd. Instead he takes her to Roland's wedding. There the gormless Roland realizes he really loves the faithful girl best – and she agrees to marry him!

6 NO! You're a princess, and princesses don't tell tales. The story is *The Goose Girl*, and that's what you've become, a humble worker. Your servant marries the prince instead. On top of that she has the only witness to her trickery – your horse, Falada – killed and its head nailed over a doorway. It's a bad mistake on her part. Falada's head gains the power of speech and the Prince discovers your secret when he overhears you talking to it. The Prince, who won't take neigh for an answer, marries you and has the servant executed in a spiked barrel.

7a) and c) . . . but not at the same time. Your name is *King Thrush-beard* and, when you turn up as yourself, the princess tells you to get lost. Hopping mad at her behaviour, the Princess's father says she'll marry the next man who comes along – and in strolls a disgusting beggar: you! You don't let on who you really are, though. Instead you take the Princess to a grotty cottage, make her sell pots in the market and finally get her a job as kitchen-maid in your own palace – by which time she's realized how daft she was to turn down that handsome being (you!) when she had the chance. That's when you reveal all. Surprise, surprise!

8 AGREE You're a witch's daughter, the one who loves you is a hunter, and the story is *The Donkey Cabbages*. The secret you steal is pretty yukky – it's a bird's heart which, while the hunter keeps it in his mouth, causes a gold coin to turn up under his pillow every morning. Stealing it is a bad move, though. The hunter tricks you and your mother into eating a mouldy cabbage – which turns you both into donkeys! It all turns out well in the end, though. After your mother is beaten to death the hunter takes pity and has you changed back into a girl again. Not surprisingly you decide you're in love with him then, and you're married at once.

9c) This happens in the story called *The Iron Stove*. The Princess gets cold feet though, and sends two other girls to try. Only when they fail does she pluck up the courage to go herself and the Prince is released. (He then disappears again, so there's a second part of the story in which she has to play hunt-the-prince before they can live happily ever after.)

10 AGREE but don't do it because, as told in the story *The Three Spinsters*, you are one smart cookie! You see three ugly women pass by. One's got a huge flat foot, one a big bottom lip reaching almost to her chin, and the third a thumb the size of a coconut. In return for an invitation to the wedding, they spin the flax for you.

Come the wedding reception the women are introduced to your new husband, the Prince. Being a tactful chap, he immediately asks them why they're so ugly. They tell him it's because they've spent their lives spinning: Flat Foot pressing the spinning wheel's pedal, Fat Lip moistening the thread and Coconut Thumb pressing it flat. The Prince immediately vows that *you* will never use a spinning wheel again!

How did you score? 8–10 Fairy, fairy good! **5–7** Fairy nough! **1–4** Tale end stuff.

Story 4: Little Red Riding Hood

Have you ever been close to a wolf?

I mean, really close. Close enough to smell its stale breath? Close enough to see its glittering teeth when it draws back its lips in a friendly little smile? Close enough to see how sharp and pointed those teeth are? Close enough to imagine what they would feel like if they bit into you . . .

No, probably not. But many people in the late 17th century certainly would have done, which is when the story in number 4 position, Red Riding Hood, first appeared in France.

But a talking wolf? Why not? Talking animals were plentiful in fairy stories. And so it's quite easy to imagine Mrs Wolf telling her husband's story to their children as she gathers them together at bedtime on a dark winter's night . . .

Who's afraid of the big bad wolf?

It all began early one morning, *purred Mrs Wolf.* Red Riding Hood was walking through the wood. Your father had often seen her. She always dressed in a dear little red riding hood, you see. So easy to spot between the dense green of the trees, he always said.

And she was so . . . how can I put it? Tasty-looking. Small, but mouth-watering. More than once he'd thought about attacking her, but she'd been lucky. The woods were alive with woodcutters, and he wasn't a wolf to take a chance. A cautious wolf, your father was.

Anyway, on this particular day, he thought of a cunning plan. Trotting up to the girl, he stopped and smiled.

"Hello, sweetie," he said to her. "And where might you be off to?"

Red Riding Hood told him she was going to visit her poor grandmother. She was carrying a basket of things for the old soul. Custard pies and pots of butter, revolting things like that. The only meat she carried was that on her own bones. But then, that's the meat your father was after . . .

"And where does the old dear live?" he said smoothly. Oh, I can see his lovely smile now!

The little girl, silly thing, went right ahead and told him. "On the other side of this wood, beyond the mill."

Your father knew the place at once, children. Quiet. Lonely. Simply perfect for an attack. No chance of any screams being heard, you see. That was most important. Humans do scream most awfully when we sink our teeth into them.

"Well, why don't I go to see her too," he said. "Let's make it a little race. I'll go my way and you go yours. We'll see who gets there first."

And off he ran . . .

Of course, your father reached the cottage first. A quick worker, he always was. And so talented. Not only could he talk, he could impersonate people. He knocked at the door and, when the old woman asked who it was, he pretended to be the girl.

"Open the door, then," she cried.

Mrs Wolf paused, making her children wait for the part that came next. Only when they were almost squealing with impatience did she continue.

So in he went, *she purred.* Oh, children, I wish I'd been there. In a trice your wonderful father had launched himself on to the woman and was tearing her apart with his strong, white teeth. My, was he hungry! It had been a difficult time, and he hadn't eaten for three days.

Well, in next to no time the only thing remaining of that grandmother was a pile of clean bones. And some of her blood, that's right. Most of it your father had licked up, but some he poured into a bottle. Such a tidy wolf, your father.

And then – oh, children, what a stroke of genius! – he put on the woman's nightcap and hopped into her bed to wait for the girl! Have you ever heard the like of it!

Eventually, along she came. Tap-tap on the door, she knocked. Once again your clever father put on a voice, this time that of the grandmother. And so, into his clutches, came tasty little Red Riding Hood . . .

Mrs Wolf's mouth was watering at the very thought of it. She had to wipe away the drips before she could continue.

And what sport he had with her! *she said finally.* For a start, and not many know this, your rascal of a father offered her a drink. Yes! Out of his little bottle! The girl

guzzled the sweet red blood of her own grandmother!

And then they had that most famous conversation, cried Mrs Wolf. Her children joined in, yelping out the lines by heart.

"Grandmother, what great arms you've got," cried the girl. So true, children! That's exactly how your father's arms were.

"All the better to embrace thee, child!" chanted Mrs Wolf's children.

"Grandmother, what great legs you've got!" He had too, laughed Mrs Wolf.

"All the better to run with, child!"

"Grandmother, what great ears you've got!" Lovely ears, *purred Mrs Wolf.* So straight, so proud.

"All the better to hear you with!" chanted the children.

"Grandmother, what great eyes you've got!" Mrs Wolf's own eyes went misty at the memory.

"All the better to see you with!"

133

"Grandmother, what great teeth you've got!" *howled Mrs Wolf joyfully.* Teeth to be proud of! Better, stronger teeth than any wolf has had before or since.

"All the better to eat you with!" cried her children, reciting the words they'd heard so often before.

Yes, *said Mrs Wolf, aglow.* And your father was a wolf of his word! In a trice he was out of that bed and soft, pink, sweet-tasting, little Red Riding Hood was being torn apart by those lovely strong teeth. Delicious! And in next to no time, that was the end of her!

The youngest of Mrs Wolf's children popped his head up. "So what happened to Papa?"

"Some of the other wolves say he was captured and chopped up."

"Nonsense," snapped Mrs Wolf. "He got clean away and came home without a scratch on him. He's not here because I threw him out."

"Why, Mama?"

"Why? Why do you think? Two humans he'd eaten! A grandmother and a child! And what did he bring me home? Nothing but a collection of bones!"

Tell Me More

Are you like Mrs Wolf at this moment – sitting there waiting for more? Well, if you insist. But what you've had up until now is exactly what the original readers had. The story of Little Red Riding Hood was a warning to children not to stray – and what more dramatic warning could there be than to end with a dead Red!

But, if you don't like that ending – and lots of tender-hearted story-tellers decided they didn't – here are three more to choose from. . .

Ending 1 (1863)

. . . The youngest of Mrs Wolf's children popped his head up. "So what happened to Papa?"

"Some of the other wolves say he was captured and chopped up."

"It's not true," Mrs Wolf said angrily. "But he was killed. And it was such bad luck. He'd polished off the bony grandmother and was just about to sink his teeth into the dreadful Red when he was stopped by a wasp stinging him on the nose!"

A tear dropped from Mrs Wolf's eye. The children could see the whole episode was still a sore point with her.

"While your dear father was reeling from the sting the wasp warned a bird, and the bird warned a hunter who saw what was happening. He at once fired an arrow. It hit your dear father in the ear and he fell dead."

Mrs Wolf shook her head sadly. "Ear today and gone tomorrow . . ."

Ending 2 (1880)

. . . The youngest of Mrs Wolf's children popped his

135

head up. "So what happened to Papa?"

"Some of the other wolves say he was captured and chopped up."

"It's true,' Mrs Wolf said angrily. "If only he hadn't been so dozy!'"

"Father? Dozy?"

"That was the undoing of him – in every way," said Mrs Wolf. "After the meal he'd had, the silly man fell asleep. He was always doing it. And when your father went to sleep nothing would wake him up. And I do mean nothing!"

"Not even thunder and lightning?"

"Not even a hunter coming up and slitting open his stomach with his knife!" cried Mrs Wolf, as if she still couldn't believe it. "Because that's what happened! Neither did your dozy dad wake up when Red Riding Hood and her wretched grandmother jumped out. Nor when they filled him up with stones! He didn't even stir when they sewed him up again!"

"When did he wake up, Mama?" asked the children.

"When the sewing was finished. That's when he jumped up, discovered he couldn't walk properly with all the stones inside him – and fell in the river!"

Mrs Wolf shook her head sadly. "What a drip . . ."

Ending 3 (1980 – Angela Carter)

. . . The youngest of Mrs Wolf's children popped his head up. "So what happened to Papa?"

"Some of the other wolves say he was captured and chopped up."

"It's not true," Mrs Wolf said angrily. "In fact . . . hardly anything of what I've told you is true! Your father wasn't a real wolf at all. He was a werewolf. He could turn into a man. He was in his man-shape when he met that awful Red girl in the woods. He only turned into a wolf when he got to the cottage."

"And ate up grandmother and Red Riding Hood? That's true, isn't it?"

"Only half true," cried Mrs Wolf. "He ate up grannie, all right. But not Red Riding Hood. Because, you see. . ."

"A hunter came and he ran off?"

"Ran off, yes. But not because a hunter turned up. Because she turned up!"

"Red Riding Hood?"

"Yes!" wailed Mrs Wolf. "She was a werewolf too. They ran off together!"

Mrs Wolf shook her head sadly. "And lived happily ever after . . ."

Top Facts 4: Animal tales

The wolf of *Little Red Riding Hood* is just one of a whole zoo of animals that turn up in fairy stories. Wild animals feature often. In some they're portrayed as majestic creatures, showing humans how to live. At other times they're both ravenous and dangerous.

You'll find plenty of less terrifying creatures, too, such as cows and birds and mice – except that they're not always as gentle as they appear.

So which is which in the animal world? Grab your binoculars and join this quick top ten trip around the safairy park!

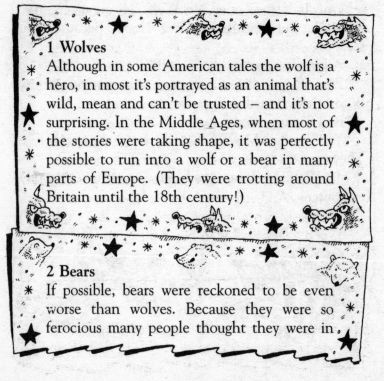

1 Wolves

Although in some American tales the wolf is a hero, in most it's portrayed as an animal that's wild, mean and can't be trusted – and it's not surprising. In the Middle Ages, when most of the stories were taking shape, it was perfectly possible to run into a wolf or a bear in many parts of Europe. (They were trotting around Britain until the 18th century!)

2 Bears

If possible, bears were reckoned to be even worse than wolves. Because they were so ferocious many people thought they were in league with the Devil. There were crazy beliefs about them, too. Bear cubs were thought to be born as shapeless furry balls which were only turned into recognizable animals through being licked by their mother. True! It's where the saying "to be licked into shape" came from!

3 Foxes

As country people who'd suffered from raids on their poultry, most listeners to fairy stories would understand why foxes are shown as being sly and cunning.

Another reason, though, is that it's long been a superstition that the fox is one of the animals a witch can turn into. Ask the people of Oxfordshire. Late in the 18th century a fox hunt near the town of Kirklington was supposed to have chased a fox right into the house of a woman thought to be a witch. There was no way the animal could possibly escape. And yet, when the hunters went in to the house, there was no sign of any fox. Only the old lady, sitting in her chair by the fire . . . .

4 Cows

Cows were associated with witches too — witches were supposed to be able to milk them from a distance! But this isn't likely to be the reason cows figured in fairy stories. They were there because country people owned them and knew just how valuable they were. Cows gave milk when they were alive, and meat when they were dead. That's why Jack's mum is so mad with him when, in *Jack and the Beanstalk*, he sells their cow for a handful of beans. No wonder he's afraid to go home and face the moo-sic!

Probably the only time a cow appears in a bad light is in an Indian story – and then it's only half true. Two brothers inherit a cow and decide to share it. The clever brother takes the rear half and gets all the milk, while the dumb brother takes the front half and has to feed it!

5 Hens and geese

Same thing with hens and geese. Both produced eggs – which meant food to eat or, if the eggs hatched, more hens and geese which could be sold. In other words, eggs meant money. So a story about a goose which lays golden eggs was one which everybody could understand.

6 Birds

Birds in general pop up often. Equally often, they're being used by witches and the like to lead people astray. Crows and magpies were favourite bad birds of the times. One superstition even had it that if you saw a magpie you should quickly look for a crow – the idea was that the two evil birds would cancel each other out!

The dove was just about the only reliably good bird around. Because of its links with Biblical stories – such as that of Noah's Ark, where it's a dove that finds land after the flood – it was reckoned to be a good sign.

7 Donkeys

A donkey in a fairy story usually means there's a dimbo about. Either it's the donkey itself, because they are usually portrayed as stubborn and stupid, or else it's somebody who's shown to be even thicker than a donkey – that is, as stupid as they come.

One of the few useful fairy-tale donkeys appears in the story *Donkey-skin*. What's so useful about it? It produces gold dung! The donkey is owned by a king who simply has to scoop the stuff up every day. Talk about rolling in it!

8 Storks

Storks live near water and water is essential to life, so storks were linked with new life. In other words, babies. The "old wives' tale" that storks bring babies (well, there were no ambulances in those days) probably comes from the same place as the German superstition that a stork flying over a house means a birth in it soon after.

Maybe this idea that storks were good with children led to the version of *Snow White* known in India. In it, the heroine isn't looked after by seven dwarves at all, but by two storks!

9 Mice

Mice and rats don't usually do too well in fairy stories. No wonder: they were pests. Nowadays you might have one as a pet, but not so long ago you had them in your house whether you liked it or not. They were everywhere, and you had a constant struggle to stop them eating your dinner or using it as a loo! (Which is why Cinderella was able to nip off and find four white mice and a rat without any trouble.)

Of the two, mice come off best, sometimes being made into heroes as a way of pointing out that size doesn't matter. Usually, though, mice are shown as they really are: little creatures with a big appetite. One story tells of a miser who hoards grain during a famine. As a result his house is invaded by thousands of starving mice who eat the grain – and the miser as well!

10 Gnats

There are few creatures that haven't turned up in a fairy story at some time. Even the hated gnat is a hero in one by Hans Christian Andersen. Called *The Wicked Prince* it tells of a prince who is the Devil in disguise. Collecting together a massive army the Prince marches on Heaven. And what sort of army is sent out to meet him – an army of gnats! Bitten to bits, the prince goes raving mad and drops down dead. (So gnat was the end of him.) Moral of the story: even the least of God's creation has been given the power to beat evil.

Story 3: Cinderella

In number three spot is Cinderella, probably the oldest fairy story of the lot. The first known version in Europe was written in 1634, but a Cinderella-like story has been found in a Chinese book dating from around 850!

Nowadays, the story we think we know is likely to be pretty close to the one published by Charles Perrault in 1697. He's the chap responsible for the golden coach, the glass slipper and many of the other pantomime details we take for granted. He's also to blame for taking out most of the nasty bits.

To get at least some of those you have to turn to the altogether grimmer version of the Brothers Grimm, dating from 1812. Called Aschenputtel (Cinder-fool), it's charming and chilling in equal measures. Here's the story told through the diaries of Cinderella and her wicked stepmother. And there are no prizes for guessing whose thoughts are chilling and whose are charming . . .

Cinderella.

Stepmother

What time do you call this!?

It is over six months since my dear mother was buried. I have visited her grave every day. There I cry bitterly, I am so sad. Even her last words, that God would look after me if I am kind and gentle, bring me little comfort. And now my father has taken another wife.....

A new husband at last! Such a pity his daughter had to be part of the deal. Still you can't have everything. Anyway my own two beautiful daughters have already put that little madam in her place – the kitchen! And they've given her such a witty name: Cinder-fool! (It was Cinder-bum at first, until I reminded them they were ladies).

Cinder-fool is what they call me, because I'm always covered in ashes through lying near the fire to keep warm. I hate them almost as much as the rats and mice who are forever nipping at my legs and leaving their droppings in the food. I wish my mother was here to help me. Still at least my father

145

still cares for me. He is going to the fayre today and asked us all if there was anything we wanted him to bring back for us. I've asked for something special.

I'm wondering if the silly girl is going mental. My new husband brought gifts back from the fayre today. My own daughters, showing the intelligence of their mother had asked for some fine clothes. What do I find the Cinder-tool had requested? The first twig to hit his head as he rode along! Wood you credit it!

A miracle has happened! As I asked, my father brought me back a branch of hazel which brushed his hat as he rode. I duly planted this in the soil of my mother's grave, watered it with my tears..... and it has grown into a tall hazel tree! What is more, high in its branches, there now sits a white bird that throws down to me whatever I wish for. I am no longer hungry! Can this bird, I wonder, be my dear mother sent back to look after me?

Exciting news! The King has proclaimed a three-day festival during which his son, the Prince, will choose a bride. We are all invited..... Cinderfool too, unfortunately. The twit wants to go, of course, but I have a plan to prevent it. I will say that she can only come with us if she separates a tub of peas and lentils. I'll give her two hours to do it in. That should sort her out! Ha-ha!

My stepmother agreed that I could go to the festival — but only if I sorted a tub of peas and lentils. Hard enough, but made much harder by the wretched woman mixing them with the cinders of the hearth.

But she reckoned without the help of my friends, the birds! They did the job for me. I <u>shall</u> go to the ball!

The disgusting little worm shall not go to the ball, even though she did pass the test I set her. And a second test, to sort twice as many peas and lentils in half

147

the time. How she did it I don't know; I expected the task to put her into a complete flap. Be that as it may, she is not coming. She has no clothes and no shoes. She will be an embarassment. I will simply forbid her to come.

I went to the first night of the festival — so there, Stepmother!

After she forbade me, I went to the hazel tree and asked the white bird for some fine clothes. At once, she threw me down a gown of silver and gold, and a pair of silken slippers. I had a lovely time

A mystery. A beautiful girl turned up on the first night of the festival and spent the whole time dancing with the Prince. When she left before the end, the Prince claims he followed her out to our pigeon-house! But when the Prince forced his way in, there was nobody to be seen.

And a similar mystery happened last night, also. The same girl arrived, dressed even more beautifully. and again she left before the end. This time the Prince said he saw her climb the large pear tree in our garden. But when we cut it down, once again no girl was to be found. What you might call a pear of mysteries!

Tonight I am going to the ball for the third time. I have wished at the tree on my mother's grave again, and my white bird has given me the finest dress and pure gold slippers you have ever seen. Once again I do not expect my stepmother and sisters to know me. But will the Prince follow me again?

I have managed to escape from both the pigeon-house and the pear tree before he found me.

This night I must be so careful. If my disobedience was revealed my stepmother would surely make my life more miserable than ever.

Ye gods, if I could find that strange girl I would make her life a misery! The Prince is smitten with her totally. So totally that, to prevent her rushing away from him a third time last night, he had the paths laid with wet tar. Still she managed to escape, but not without leaving one of her golden slippers stuck in the tar. Now the Prince says he'll marry whomsoever it fits!

Whomsoever it fits? Now, there's a thought......

I saw the Prince arrive not long since. He was bearing my golden slipper.

Now I hear the sound of rejoicing. I wonder what's happened?

A triumph! A veritable triumph! I went to my lovely elder daughter's chamber as she tried on the slipper. It didn't fit, her big toe was too large. And what was the stupid girl about to do? Return

150

to the Prince and say as much.

"Nay, daughter." I said producing a knife. "Cut off that toe and it will surely fit."

Oh her blood ran freely and she wailed greatly about never being able to walk again, but as I said: "Stop your caterwauling! when you're Queen you won't need to walk; you'll be carried everywhere."

And so, now able to get the slipper on, down she went— and the Prince has just ridden off with her to make her his bride!

From the grimy kitchen window I can see the fair Prince. I see my elder sister also. They are stopped at my hazel tree with the white bird. I wonder why?

A triumph turned into a disaster! No sooner had the Prince and my elder daughter left than they were back again. Some busybody of a bird in a tree had pointed out the blood oozing from the slipper and the Prince had realized he'd been tricked.

151

So back upstairs I went with younger daughter! She tried the slipper, but her heel wouldn't fit. Bah! Similar problem, similar solution! Out came the knife again. A few slices, not much more than a couple of rashers of bacon (and yet, an amazing ammount of blood again) and it was done. On with the slipper—and the Prince was fooled once more. Off he's ridden with younger daughter for his bride!

From the grimy kitchen window I can see the fair Prince again. This time I see my younger stepsister with him. They have also stopped at my hazel tree with the white bird. I wonder why?

Rip out my entrails and use them for a wash-line! Cut out my kidneys and use them for pin cushions! Never have I been so humiliated!

No sooner had the Prince left than he was back. Once again the same bird had pointed out the bloody slipper and for a second time he'd realized he'd been tricked!

Worse, my idiot of a husband mentioned Cinder-fool and he insisted on having her try the slipper. And it fit her to perfection! It transpires that she was the mystery girl at the festival — though where she got her clothes from really is a mystery.

The only consolation is that we're all invited to the wedding.

A wondrous day! Our marriage went off splendidly with only one disturbance of note. My stepsisters, who were serving as bridesmaids, were attacked by birds and had their eyes pecked out.

I can only imagine this was due to their wickedness towards me. I can't see that it could be for anything else.

And neither can they, now.

Tell me more

That's it, my dears. The nasty ending is over. You can open your eyes, now – which is more than the sisters can! Ha-ha-ha!

Top Facts 3: You shall go to the ball!

White mice and pumpkins, glittering coaches and polished Buttons, wicked stepmothers and ugly sisters ... where did they come from, and are they to be found in every Cinderella story?

The answer is: no, they're not. It's reckoned that about 700 versions of the Cinderella story exist throughout the world. That is, stories which tell of a poor girl who's banished to the kitchen but ends up marrying a prince who spots her by the size of her tootsies.

But there are lots of differences – as you'll discover in this top ten Cinder-facts ...

1 Cinderella's name in English shouldn't be "Cinderella"! The name Cinderella comes from the French version of the story written by Charles Perrault, in which the heroine is called Cendrillon – from the French word, *cendre*. What does it mean?

Answer:

Ashes – because ashes are what she lived amongst. So her name in English should really be "Ash-ella"!

ASHELLA? ......
....THAT DOESN'T
SOUND TOO HOT!

2 Cinders, ashes – they're the same, aren't they? Not for the listeners they wouldn't have been. Cinders are just the dirty remnants of a fire, but ashes had been a sign of something in particular since Biblical times. A sign of what?

Answer:

Mourning. People would smear themselves with ash to show that somebody they loved had died. So the listeners would have realized at once that Cinderella's name, and the fact that she slept amongst the ashes, was a sign that she was still mourning for her mother.

COULDN'T I JUST WEAR BLACK FOR A CHANGE?

3 The earliest known "Cinderella" is named Yeh-sien, and she's the heroine of a Chinese story that's 1000 years old. After her mother and father both die, she's badly treated by her other-mother (men could take more than one wife). Yeh-sien's only friend is her huge pet fish, which she talks to every day – until it's killed and eaten by the wicked mother! The mother makes a big mistake, though. What is it?

Answer:

She leaves the fish-bones. Yeh-sien saves them and whenever she prays to them her wishes are granted! To go to a local festival, she wishes herself a cloak of kingfisher feathers and a pair of gold slippers. There she loses one of the slippers – but not to a prince, to a cave dweller! He sells the slipper, as does the next person, and so on until it's finally bought by a war-lord who orders that his kingdom should be searched for the girl whose foot it fits.

I WOULD HAVE EATEN THE BONES AS WELL BUT THEY ALWAYS GIVE ME A SPLITTING HADDOCK!

4 Another version of the story was known in Scotland as long ago as 1540. In this story the heroine is *Rashin Coatie* – meaning "coat of rushes", after the nasty item that she's forced to wear as she slaves for her sisters. Again, there isn't a fairy godmother in sight nor a magic fish. Rashin Coatie's helper is – what?

Answer:

A little red calf her dying mother gave her. Stepmother finds out about it and the little thing's butchered. Then, as in the Chinese story, Rashin Coatie buries its bones and prays to them to get what she needs, including the outfit which enables her to go to the Prince's party and lose one of her satin slippers.

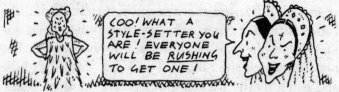

5 Ever wondered why the slipper shouldn't have fitted dozens of likely brides? It's not so unlikely if the story began in China. There, for a girl's feet to be the right size was a sign of great beauty. But what size?

Answer:

As small as possible. Chinese girls' feet were bound to stop them growing. That's why only Yeh-sien's foot fitted the slipper; nobody else's was as small, because nobody else was as beautiful. Cinderellas have been following in her footsteps ever since!

6 Until Charles Perrault wrote his version in 1695, Cinderella's slipper had always been made of felt or some soft material such as satin. But then Perrault turned it into a slipper made of glass. Why?

Answer:

He made a mistake! It's thought that when he first heard the story the slipper was made of fur ("vair" in French) but that he wrote down glass ("verre") instead because the two French words sound the same. Whether this is true or not, he obviously decided that a glass slipper was perfect for the story because, unlike fur or any other soft material, there was no way it could be stretched by an ugly sister's foot.

7 Perrault also invented many of the other parts of the Cinderella story we know today. The fairy godmother was his idea, and so was turning mice into footmen and being home by midnight. He also ended his version with a verse pointing out the moral of the story.

"Beautiful ladies, it's kindness more than dress
That wins a man's heart with greater success.
So, if you want a life filled with bliss,
The truest gift is . . ."

What's the missing word?

Answer:

Graciousness. That is, it doesn't matter what you look like, it's what's inside that counts. A gracious person has good manners and all that stuff, even if she does look awful.

8 But the really awful-looking ones were Cinderella's sisters, weren't they? The *ugly* sisters?

Answer:

No. In most early versions of Cinderella, the sisters were beautiful to look at. Their ugliness was in the way they acted.

9 Nowadays the character of "Buttons" is almost as much a part of the story as Cinderella herself. In which written version did he first turn up?

Answer:

He didn't! Buttons started to creep into the story after 1804, the year in which it was first staged as a pantomime. Why? Because it helped the audience to have Cinderella telling somebody about her problems. Enter Buttons – and the heroine didn't have to button her lip any longer!

10 One thing's never changed, though. Cinderella has always been shown as good, kind, sweet, lovely, wonderful, adorable, etc. etc. etc. Hasn't she?

Answer:

Er . . . no, not exactly. In an Italian version of the story called *The Hearth Cat* which appeared in 1634, Cinderella (she's named Zezolla in this story) doesn't suffer at the hands of her stepmother at all. Why not? Because she murders her! Together with her governess, Zezolla tricks her stepmother into looking in a chest for some clothes, then slams the lid down on her and breaks her neck! Zezolla persuades her father to take the governess as his wife, and it's then that Zezolla finds out she's been tricked. The governess has six daughters and it's they who make her life a misery as the story continues in familiar fashion.

Story 2: Jack and the Beanstalk

Tale number two is Jack and the Beanstalk. This story, which dates from 1730, is English. It's one of a number of "Jack tales" all of which star a boy who's thick or lazy – or both.

The sort of boy, in fact, who would have been sent home with some terrible school reports to think about and add his own comments to . . .

Bottom of the class
THE VILLAGE SCHOOL
REPORT ON: JACK

GENERAL
Teacher's Comments: Jack is anything but a jack-of-all-trades. In fact, he's the laziest boy I've ever had in this school. He's bone idle and completely stupid. I don't know why his mother puts up with his behaviour.

Pupil's Comments: She puts up with it because I'm her favourite son! Come to think of it, I'm her only son....

BIOLOGY

Teacher's Comments: Jack shows no understanding in biology at all. I'd be surprised if he knew the difference between an animal and a vegetable.

Pupil's Comments: I disagree! And I'll prove it! A while ago my mother sent me off to the next village to sell our cow. We'd got no money left, see. Anyway, on the road I met this butcher who made me a bargain offer: a hat full of beans! I said yes straight away and took 'em home to Mum. What did she say? "You great turnip!" So there you go. I do know the difference. A cow's an animal and I'm a vegetable.

MUM

PHYSICAL EDUCATION

Teacher's Comments: Jack is lazy. He'll never reach any heights in the sporting world until he stops sitting around all day dreaming.

Pupil's Comments: I disagree! And I'll prove it! My mother was so angry about the beans she threw them out of the window. Next morning, what have the beans been and done? Grown! And I do mean grown. The beanstalk stretched right up into the sky — a lot higher than the ropes we use for P.E. that's for sure! And I climbed right to the very top! So there you go. I didn't spend that day dreaming, did I? I had my head the clouds instead.

GEOGRAPHY

Teacher's Comments: Hopeless! Jack doesn't know one country from another. And judging by his attendance record he could do with a map to help him find the school! I really don't think Jack has much chance of finding his way in life.

Pupil's Comments: I disagree! And I'll prove it! When I got to the top of the beanstalk I found I <u>was</u> in a different country. What's more, I met a nice lady (not a mouldy one like some I could mention) who told me my life story. She said we had pots of money once, until a giant murdered my dad. He'd only spared me and my Mum because she'd promised not to say anything to me about it. Then she said I was the one who was meant to sort out the giant! So she told me the way to his castle and off I went.

I found it by sunset, so there! Maybe if school started at night instead of in the morning I'd get there on time as well.

COOKERY

Teacher's Comments: Jack is always in a stew with this subject. The bread he made tasted awful. He couldn't possibly have been working from a recipe.

Pupil's Comments: I disagree! And I'll prove it! When I reached the giant's castle his wife answered the door. She didn't want to let me in at first, because she said the giant wasn't a vegetarian and I'd be just the sort of meal he'd fancy. But I talked her into it and she hid me in the oven. When her husband came home,

though, I found out what she meant.
In he came, singing a song. It went :-

FEE, FI, FO, FUM,
I SMELL THE BLOOD OF AN
ENGLISHMAN
BE HE ALIVE OR BE HE DEAD
I'LL GRIND HIS BONES TO
MAKE ME BREAD

"It's just the humans you've got stored down in the cold, cold cellar," his wife told him. So there you are! That's one thing I know about cookery — you have to keep your meat in the fridge.

Anyway, after that he had his dinner then called for his hen. I thought he was going to eat that too, but no. He put it in front of him and said, "Lay." So then I thought he must fancy a nice egg with a golden yolk instead, but no. When the egg came out the whole thing was made of gold!

Honest, Miss, I'm not yolking! He did this a few times, then fell asleep. That's when I crept out, grabbed the hen and raced back to the beanstalk and home.

So there you go, I do know something about cookery. And I did use a recipe for my bread, Miss. It was the giant's recipe, but with "a few dog's bones. Well you wouldn't have wanted me to use my own, would you?

MATHEMATICS

Teacher's Comments: Jack is so useless at arithmetic I swear he doesn't even know how many beans make five. He doesn't seem to realize he needs to be able to count if he's ever going to get a well-paid job. He'll never make any money by using his hands and feet.

Pupil's Comments: I disagree! And I'll prove it! The second time I climbed the beanstalk and went to the giant's castle his wife let me in again. This time while I was in hiding, the giant pulled out two great bags, one of gold and one of silver. He spent all night counting how much he had.

When he fell asleep I nipped out, grabbed the bags and ran for it. If that's not making money using my hands and feet I don't know what is!

MUSIC

Teacher's Comments: Jack knows nothing about music. He doesn't even take notes, let alone play them, because the lessons are after school and he doesn't waste any time at all in running off.

Pupil's Comments: This time I DO agree! And it's just as well! I'll prove it! I went a third time to the giant's castle and hid while he was eating his supper. This time when he'd finished he got his wife to bring him his harp to play on. Well, the giant didn't play it exactly. It was a magic harp. All the giant did was say, "Play!" and the harp played a tune all on it's own. Brilliant! Just the instrument for me I thought.

So when the giant went to sleep, I grabbed it. And what happened? The harp started squawking, "Master! Master!" and woke the giant up! In a minute he was on his feet and running after me...

So there you go, Miss. You can stop harping on about this subject as well. There was no way I was going to stick around to face the music!

FIRST-AID

Teacher's Comments: Here, at last, is a subject for which Jack at least shows some enthusiasm. What a pity he's useless at it. In the practical class he was the one person who correctly diagnosed my swollen ankle as a sprain. Unfortunately, his suggested remedy was to chop it off.

Pupil's Comments: I disagree! And I'll prove it! Escaping from the giant the third time I raced down to the bottom of the beanstalk. But when I looked up I saw he was coming down after me! So quick a flash I grabbed an axe and chopped the beanstalk down. The giant fell from the sky and landed in a heap stone dead.

So there you go! I examined him, Miss, and his neck was definately broken. Not sprained, broken. I may be a pain in the neck, but I do know the difference.

Parent's Comments: EVERYTHING JACK'S SAID IS TRUE! HE KILLED THE GIANT AND NOW WE HAVE PLENTY OF MONEY. SO MUCH MONEY, IN FACT, THAT HE DOESN'T HAVE TO GO TO SCHOOL ANY MORE!

P.S. IF YOU WOULD LIKE A DEAD GIANT TO DISPLAY AT THE SCHOOL SUMMER FAYRE, PLEASE LET ME KNOW. THERE'S NO CHARGE, BUT YOU WILL HAVE TO COLLECT HIM YOURSELF.

Head Teacher's Comments: I have read this report with much interest and can draw only one conclusion from it. Jack may be a complete idiot at most subjects but when it comes to making up stories there's nobody to beat him.

Tell me more

- Early illustrations for *Jack and the Beanstalk* were very babyish. One of them, dating from 1734, shows a tiny Jack climbing a beanstalk which isn't much higher than their cottage – and the castle at the top wouldn't house a doll, let alone a giant!

- There are many other "Jack" tales in England. *The History of Jack and the Giants* dates from around 1700 and is really a collection of tales about a fairy-tale "Giant-Buster" who roams the country cleaning up giants that nobody else has been able to deal with.

  One is a Cornish giant, 6 metres high and 3 metres wide. Jack polishes him off by digging a giant-sized pit then waking him up. The stupid giant rushes at Jack, and falls in the pit – after which all Jack has to do is hammer a pick-axe into the giant's head, then fill the hole in.

- For more of a challenge Jack then takes on a couple of giants together, even though he's been locked in a tower by one of them, Blunderboar, a giant whose favourite snack is a man's heart sprinkled with pepper and vinegar. (In other words, he had good taste!)

  Waiting until Blunderboar and his friend pass beneath him, Jack throws a noose round their necks, tosses the end over a high beam in his cell and pulls it hard. When the giants stop struggling Jack slides down the rope and, just in case they're not fully hanged, runs them through with his sword.

- A Welsh giant gives Jack a harder time. Pretending to be friendly, he gives Jack a bed for the night. Smelling a rat, though, Jack puts a pillow in the bed instead and curls up in the corner. Good move. During the night in creeps the giant and gives the pillow a good thumping.

Next morning, to the giant's surprise, Jack appears at breakfast saying that he slept well – apart from a rat tickling him with its tail. He then joins the giant for breakfast and appears to scoff large amounts of porridge, although he's actually tipping the stuff into a bag hidden inside his coat. When the giant asks how he can eat so much, Jack says that when he gets full he cuts himself open, lets the porridge run out, then starts again! Taking a knife, he then cuts open the bag. Of course, brainy Mr Giant says "anyone can do that" and, as it says in the version published in 1711 . . .

> *"Taking a sharp knife he ripped open his own belly from the bottom to the top, and out dropped his tripes and trolly-bubs . . ."*

Just in case you're wondering, the giant's "tripes" would be parts of his stomach. As for his "trolly-bubs", your guess is as revolting as mine!

Top Facts 2: A world of weirdos

Just as "Jack" tales are common throughout the world, so are giants and witches and all manner of other fairy-tale villains.

How villainous? So villainous that, if they really existed, every police force would have descriptions of them on a terrible top ten of "wanted" posters.

Descriptions such as these, in the villains' own words . . .

1. Name: Black Annis
Country: England
Description: Considering I live in a cave, I'm one of the best-looking hags in the business. I've got a set of long teeth, which look really white against my blue face. My favourite pastime is keeping  an eye out for people – dead easy, because one eye is all I've got! Tasty children and lonesome travellers are my favourites. I catch them in my claws of iron and eat them.

2. Name: Bunyip
Country: Australia
Description: G'day! I'm a large, black monster. That's right! Oh yes, and I'm amphibious. That means I can get you on land or I can get you in the water. That's why I live in a swamp, 'cos it's a bit of

both. How will you know if you meet me? Well, apart from my very distinctive looks, I give loud cries as I move around. Not as loud as the women and children I eat, though!

3. Name: Drac
Country: France
Description: I'm a little sneaky water creature and if you want to meet me then you'll have to go searching for treasure in a nice echoing little river cavern. Keep your eyes open for something that looks like a

glittering piece of gold – it could be me! How will you know for sure? Reach down and try to pick up the gold piece. If your arm is grabbed and you're dragged under the water and drowned in a flood of bubbles then you've found me, you lucky thing!

4. Name: Friar Rush
Country: Germany
Description: I'b a shpirit. A very nishe shpirit, shome would shay. Wod I do ish live

in heople'sh pouses, I mean people'sh houshes, and get them dronk, I mean drink, I mean drunk. Hic!

5. Name: Gwyllion
Country: Wales
Description: I'm a fairy, see. Not one of your pretty fairies, mind, a horrible one with looks to match. Sometimes, just to fool people, I turn myself into a goat. Then I act  the goat! Night-time travellers on the most dangerous Welsh roads are my favourites. I make them lose their way so they're still travelling next morning!

6. Name: Bodach
Country: Scotland
Description: Och, I shouldn't be with this lot. I'm just a shrivelled, wrinkled old bogeyman who spends his days warming his toes by the fire. So, I'm hiding in the chimney, but I  find it's comfortable there. And if you're not a wicked child then that's where I'll stay. You *are* wicked, your teacher never stops saying so? Och,

then that's different. Come night-time I'll be hopping down that chimney and into your bedroom – and you, wicked child, will have the most terrible, terrible nightmares!

7. Name: Kappa
Country: Japan

Description: Some people say I'm odd. So, I've got the body and shell of a tortoise, the legs of a frog and the head of a monkey – oh, yes, and my head's got a hole in the top? But that's not an odd look, not for a water demon. I know I catch swimming humans and eat them. For a water demon that's not odd either. How do I eat them? All right, I admit it. I start from the inside and eat my way outwards. That *is* odd. Tasty, though.

8. Name: Cigouaves
Country: Haiti

Description: Are you a lad? Good. You're the sort of human I like. Not that you'll see me. I do what I do to you during the night, under the cover of darkness, when you're under the covers, fast asleep. And what do I do to you? I'll give you a clue. I cut something off with the very sharp knife I carry. What do I cut off? You'll find that out first thing in the morning when you try to go to the loo! Come on, go to sleep. Chop, chop!

9. Name: Ajatar
Country: Finland
Description: Big head. Bigger body. Long tail. More scales than a weighing machine factory. Breathes more fire than a headmistress on the warpath. You've got it – I'm a lady dragon. That's  why what I do is *so* right. I spread diseases that give people a burning fever!

10. Name: Baba Yaga
Country: Russia
Description: Saving the best till last, of course! My name is Baba Yaga, the ogress with the mostest! Children just love me. They're always finding their way to my little hut in the woods. Well, that's

not quite true. It's my little hut that finds its way to them. It's got legs you see, like a chicken's, and can move quickly to where the children are. What you might call a fast food restaurant! Because that's what I do, you see. I eat them. Oh, it's all over very quickly. My stone teeth are in perfect condition. I've never had a filling!

Story 1: Sleeping Beauty

And so we come to our top, our number one tale. Sleeping Beauty.

Have you enjoyed those you've read so far? I do hope so. I also hope you've discovered by now that the stories you thought you knew actually started life rather differently – and, often, rather horribly.

So, let's finish with a gentle, heart-warming story, shall we? A story of evil overcome by a dashing prince who wakes an enchanted maiden with a kiss. For that's what happens in Sleeping Beauty, isn't it?

Er . . . no, it isn't actually. Not in the version told by the Italian, Basile, dating from 1636 it isn't. Forget all that romantic stuff, especially where the Prince is concerned. Sleeping Beauty? You won't sleep at all after this one! This is a tale that's as nasty as all the rest.

So nasty that I think I'll tell it myself. *Once upon a time* . . .

While you were asleep ...

... there lived, in this very ruined castle where we're sitting now, a king and a queen. The castle wasn't ruined then, of course. It was a joyful place, full of light – and especially when Their Majesty's dear little daughter was born. They named her Talia.

Now, being anxious about what the future held for their daughter, the King and Queen summoned all the wise men in the land to the palace and asked them to predict what would happen to Talia in the years to come. And the wise men all foresaw that Talia would die through being pricked by a splinter while spinning flax.

Is it any wonder then, that their majesties at once banned spinning wheels and everything of that kind from the palace? But it was all to no avail.

For one day years later, exploring on her own, Talia went to a room at the very top of the highest tower of the palace. There she found an old woman. She hadn't heard of any proclamation and was busy working at a spinning wheel. Fascinated, Talia asked if she could try it for herself. Straight away a splinter pierced the skin beneath her fingernail and she fell down dead. Quite, quite dead.

Come with me. There, you see this little room? It was here that Talia's grief-stricken parents laid her out on a bed of velvet before abandoning their palace to the weeds and brambles . . .

The years passed. And then, one day, a king from a distant land rode by. He'd been hunting, and his falcon had flown into the palace. When it didn't return, he followed – and discovered Talia.

Now this, I'm afraid, is where the story begins to get a little – how shall I put it? – seedy. This was not one of your more polite and chivalrous kings. As he saw Talia, he was *at once captivated by her beauty. Nothing wrong with that. He tried to wake her up. Nothing wrong with that, either.*

But climb into bed with her, then gallop off home to his own queen (because he was already married)? Hardly the act of a gentleman! But, I'm sorry to say, that's exactly what happened . . .

Nine months later, Talia gave birth to twins. Double trouble you might think, but no . . . it was one of these little darlings who revived their mother. Mighty hungry, it sucked her finger and out came the splinter. Talia woke up . . .

Not so long later, that ungentlemanly king rode by once more. Was he ashamed at what he'd done? Not a bit of it! He freely admitted to Talia what had gone on, and offered to support her and the twins. They named the children "Sun" and "Moon" and they all moved to the king's palace . . .

. . . And into the clutches of the king's mother, the twins' grandmother. Talia may

have forgiven the king for what he did, but his mother definitely hadn't. And to prove it, she was cooking up a punishment for all concerned – and I do mean "cooking".

When Sun and Moon arrived at the palace, she took them into her care. In no time at all, they were on their way to the kitchen to meet the chef. And dear grandmother's instructions were quite clear. The chef was to . . .

1 *Slit the children's throats.*

2 *Slice the flesh from their bones.*

3 *Feed it through the mincer.*

4 *Add spices, herbs and the like to taste.*

5 *Cook thoroughly, stirring well – and, finally. . .*

6 *Feed the whole lot to her son, the king. . .*

Dinner-time that evening found grandmother in a cheerful mood. "Eat it all up," she cackled when the dish was placed before the king. "It is your own!"

So the king polished it off, smacked his lips, and asked for seconds. Only then did his wicked mother explain what she'd meant about it being "his own" – that he'd just eaten his own children.

The king rushed off – and only then, to his great relief, did he discover the truth. He hadn't eaten his children after all. Fortunately for Sun and Moon, the chef's heart had been kinder than Grandmother's. Unable to bring himself to butcher the twins, he'd made the dish from a couple of lambs instead.

In no time at all, however, Grandmother found out the truth herself. Spitting with fury she set off to finish the job. Talia was captured. Was she destined to be cooked as well? After a fashion. Grandmother's orders for her were that she should be burned alive. Saved from a poisoned splinter, only to end up tied to a well-done stake!

There was only one thing Talia could do, she decided: put things off for as long as possible in the hope that help would come.

"I must undress first," she said.

"Very well," agreed Grandmother. "After all, there's no point in ruining a fine set of clothes. The gold and pearl embroidery on that gown you're wearing is worth something even if you're not."

And so Talia began one of the few fairy-tale strip-tease acts ever devised . . .

She slowly took off her gown. But no help came.

She slowly took off her skirt. Still there was no sign of help.

She took off her blouse, slowly of course. Still there was no sign of help, and Talia was starting to feel helpless.

She started to take off her petticoat . . . when help arrived! Into the room rushed the king to save her!!

They all lived happily ever after, you think? Yes, they did, but not straight away. Wicked Grandmother was still plotting, waiting for another day, a day when her son the king was away on business. Finally the day arrived, and at once she set about executing her plan. What was it? To have an execution, of course.

She had a huge tub brought into the courtyard of the palace and filled to the brim with wriggling, jiggling poisonous snakes. Talia, Sun and Moon, the chef who'd disobeyed her orders – and his family for good measure – were all herded in with their hands tied behind their backs.

But, just as they're were about to be tossed into the tub, back came the king to save the day once again!

This was simply too much for the evil Grandmother. With a cry of anguish she dived into the tub herself and was eaten alive by the snakes.

<u>Then</u> they all lived happily ever after.

Tell me more

- A version published in 1729 changed things about. Gone were the wise men and their predictions at the beginning, and in came a witch who put a curse on the Princess as revenge for not being invited to her christening.

   Why the change? Perhaps because making predictions was seen as the work of the Devil. In England it was actually a crime to make certain types of prediction. In 1530, Henry VIII passed a law forbidding anybody to predict the death of the monarch. This came too late to save a hermit named Peter the Wise who in 1213 predicted the death of King John. This made him guilty of sorcery *and* treason – both hanging offences. Not very wise, Peter!

- The naughty king was quickly turned into a much nicer chap too. He became a charming prince who simply woke Sleeping Beauty, only becoming the father of her children after they'd fallen in love. This meant that Grandmother really didn't have much reason to eat them, of course. No problem – she was turned into an ogress disguised as a grandmother!

- One familiar touch didn't arrive for another hundred years, though. Until 1827, Beauty simply woke up when the Prince arrived and said hello. It was only when the tale was turned into a pantomime that he began to work the magic feat by kissing her.

Top Facts 1: Fairy stories today

It wouldn't be right to end this book without pointing out that fairy tales aren't simply stories that were told and written down hundreds of years ago. They're still being told today.

Try this top ten quiz to find out where and how!

1 One of the most well-known fairy tales today wasn't written until the 20th century, being first performed as a play in 1904. Which tale?
a) The Ugly Duckling
b) Babes in the Wood
c) Peter Pan

2 Ever been to the theatre to see a pantomime? Then you've almost certainly watched a modern version of a fairy tale! Turning fairy tales into pantomimes has been going on for years as you can see from this top list of when each was first performed.

1788	Aladdin
1793	Babes in the Wood
1803	Little Red Riding Hood
1804	Cinderella
1806	Mother Goose
1810	Puss in Boots
1814	Dick Whittington
1819	Jack and the Beanstalk
1822	Sleeping Beauty
????	Snow White

That's the question. In what year was the pantomime *Snow White* first staged?

3 Many films have been based on fairy tales. Which was the inspiration for both the films *King Kong* (in which a giant gorilla kidnaps a beautiful explorer-lady), and *The Hunchback of Notre Dame* (in which a deformed bell-ringer falls for a beautiful peasant-lady)?
a) Sleeping Beauty
b) Beauty and the Beast
c) Little Red Riding Hood

4 And what were the popular *Home Alone* films all about? The classic fairy-tale theme of children being abandoned by their parents, of course, such as the story of *Babes in the Wood*. In the modern pantomime version, the children are left in Sherwood Forest and rescued by Robin Hood and his Merry Men. But was this the original storyline – YES or NO?

5 Modern authors have used fairy-tale themes, such as giants. One of the most famous stories is Roald Dahl's *The BFG* (Big Friendly Giant). In this story the heroine, Sophie, plays a "Jack the Giant Killer" role with the BFG helping her against a bunch of child-eating giants. Which of Jack's tricks do they use to win the day?

a) Hang them by the neck until they're dead.
b) Trap them in a huge pit.
c) Trick them into cutting their own stomachs open.

6 *The Narnia Chronicles*, the famous books by C.S.Lewis, have all the ingredients of fairy tales: they are set in a magical world (Narnia) of castles and woods; they have child heroes and heroines; they have witches and nasty creatures.

One difference, at least at the opening of the stories, is that they begin in England and the children travel to Narnia. How?

a) Through a wardrobe.
b) Through a picture.
c) They're summoned by a character living in Narnia.

7 Do you know somebody who wears a charm bracelet? How about somebody who has a St Christopher medal? Or a rabbit's foot? They're all supposed to bring the wearer good luck (although the rabbit's foot couldn't have brought the rabbit much) and come from the same Middle Ages superstitions which found their way into fairy tales.

The same goes for the latest body-piercing fashions! In the Middle Ages, wearing a ring through your nose was all the rage! Why?

a) It was thought to stop you catching a cold.
b) It was thought to improve your sense of smell.

c) It was thought to keep out evil spirits.

8 A sure sign that a story has become truly famous is when references to it creep into everyday speech – which is exactly what's happened with lots of fairy tales. When lowly football teams beat higher sides they're called "giant-killers", and if they're poor and usually unnoticed they're called a "Cinderella outfit" as well.

But what if somebody calls you an "ugly duckling"? What do you do?

a) Punch them in the nose.

b) Say, "Thanks!"

c) Wait for a few years before deciding whether to do **a)** or **b)**.

9 You're told a joke beginning: "There was an Englishman, an Irishman and a Scotsman . . ." Why is it like a fairy story?

10 Are fairy stories unfair-y . . . to girls? Critics have suggested this, complaining that stories like Cinderella give the idea that a girl's one aim in life should be to find a rich husband.

So in 1994 a new version of *Cinderella* was published. How did it end?

a) Cinderella didn't go to the ball, she stayed at home

and had a party with her friends.

b) Cinderella got dressed up to go to the ball but when midnight came she decided her rags were more comfortable.

c) Cinderella didn't marry the prince at all, she just went off and lived with him.

Answers:

1c) Check out the list in Top Facts 2 and you'll see that *Peter Pan* has got just about everything a fairy tale could want: a hero (Peter), a heroine (Wendy), a nasty villain (Captain Hook), a helpful animal (the Crocodile!), and a good, if irritable, fairy (Tinker Bell). It's even got a witches' brew of sorts: Captain Hook tries to poison the hero by adding some of his own yellow blood to Peter's medicine!

2 1950. Until the Disney cartoon of *Snow White* was made in 1938, the fairy tale wasn't at all popular. The pantomime only became a favourite after the success of the film.

3b) They're both examples of "Beauty and the Beast" stories.

4 NO. As first written, *The Children (Babes) in the Wood* was a tragedy worthy of Shakespeare. Two children are left in the care of their uncle who will inherit all their money if they die. Surprise, surprise: the uncle hires two killers to take the children out into the woods and finish them off. One of them changes his mind though, murders his mate and lets the children go. Off they trot – only to starve to death! The wicked uncle doesn't win either. He loses all the money he's stolen and ends up dying in prison. Jolly!

5b) . . . which is then filled in with earth and the rotten giants suffocate.

6a), b) and **c)** The author uses all three methods in the seven books which make up the series. The wardrobe is only used in the most famous, *The Lion, The Witch and the Wardrobe*. Of all the stories, this one is most like a fairy tale. Narnia is frozen – a wicked enchantment by a witch. This enchantment is undone by the children using magic items they're given: weapons, and an elixir that can cure anything. And what happens at the end? The children become kings and queens and go to live in a castle.

7c) Evil spirits were supposed to be able to sneak into your body through your nose. Sticking a lucky ring through it was the way to keep them out!

8c) You're not being insulted, they're referring to Hans Christian Andersen's fairy tale *The Ugly Duckling* about a scruffy little "duck" who actually grows up to be a beautiful swan. They're saying you may not be much to look at now, but you're going to be a beautiful babe/handsome hunk in a few years' time. So *wait* – and if you turn out to be an ugly old duck, then punch them on the nose!

9 Because it's using the idea of "three", in this case three men.

10b) What's more, in the (joke) version written by James Finn Garner in his book *Politically Correct Bedtime Stories*, all the other women at the ball decide they've had enough of squeezing themselves into uncomfortable clothes just to look nice for men, so they change into scruffy gear as well!

The End

Fairy tales are important. They're part of our history.

Each tale tells us something about the time in which it was told. That's true as much today as it was hundreds of years ago. The best stories are changed to keep them up to date, but they still go on being told – just as they have been in this book.

That's the way it's always been, and always will be.

Why? Because, deep down, fairy tales are about you and me. They're about our hopes and our fears. They're about what makes us laugh, and what makes us hide under the bedclothes! They're about right and wrong. They're about good and evil.

That's why youngsters (and adults if they're brave enough to admit it) still love fairy stories.

You don't believe me?

Then why do you think I wrote this book?

And why have you just read it?

THAT WAS EXCELLENT! EVEN IF THERE WASN'T A SINGLE FAIRY IN IT!